# Answer Book

Rigby
Halley Court, Jordan Hill, Oxford, OX2 8EJ
a division of Reed Educational and Professional Publishing Ltd

Rigby is a registered trademark of Reed Educational and Professional Publishing Ltd

OXFORD   MELBOURNE   AUCKLAND
JOHANNESBURG   BLANTYRE   GABORONE
IBADAN   PORTSMOUTH (NH)   CHICAGO

First published 1999

04   03   02   01   00
10  9  8  7  6  5  4  3

ISBN 0 435 216805

Designed and typeset by Gecko Limited, Bicester, Oxon
Illustrated by Gecko Limited and Harvey Collins
Printed and bound by Ashford Press, Gosport

# Contents

This *Answer Book* contains answers to the following components of Numeracy Focus:

## CFB ▪ 1a

Children's answers may vary.

## CFB ▪ 1b

From door 1, the children should reach room 680. Their prize is a crown.

From door 10, the children reach room 848. Their prize is a torch.

From door 100, the children reach room 1478. Their prize is a skull.

## CFB ▪ 1c

76 squares, 120 stars, 160 circles.

## CFB ▪ 2a

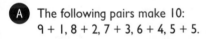 The following pairs make 10:
9 + 1, 8 + 2, 7 + 3, 6 + 4, 5 + 5.

The following pairs make 13:
12 + 1, 11 + 2,
10 + 3, 9 + 4, 8 + 5, 7 + 6.

The following pairs make 16:
13 + 3, 12 + 4, 11 + 5, 10 + 6,
9 + 7, 8 + 8.

**B** 
| **1.** 22 | **2.** 23 | **3.** 21 |
| **4.** 26 | **5.** 22 | |

## CFB ▪ 2b

**A** The following pairs make 40:
30 + 10, 20 + 20.

The following pairs make 70:
60 + 10, 50 + 20, 40 + 30.

The following pairs make 90:
80 + 10, 70 + 20, 60 + 30, 50 + 40.

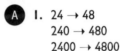

| First stone | Second stone |
| --- | --- |
| 50 | 30 |
| 800 | 900 |
| 70 | 90 |
| 1500 | 1400 |
| 1200 | 800 |

## CFB ▪ 2c

**A**
1.  24 → 48
    240 → 480
    2400 → 4800

2.  13 → 26
    130 → 260
    1300 → 2600

3.  32 → 64
    320 → 640
    3200 → 6400

4.  41 → 82
    410 → 820
    4100 → 8200

5.  12 → 24
    120 → 240
    1200 → 2400

6.  22 → 44
    220 → 440
    2200 → 4400

7.  44 → 88
    440 → 880
    4400 → 8800

8.  50 → 100
    500 → 1000
    5000 → 10 000

**B** 1. $18 \leftarrow 36 \rightarrow 72$
2. $14 \leftarrow 28 \rightarrow 56$
3. $170 \leftarrow 340 \rightarrow 680$
4. $23 \leftarrow 46 \rightarrow 92$
5. $2300 \leftarrow 4600 \rightarrow 9200$
6. $190 \leftarrow 380 \rightarrow 760$
7. $1700 \leftarrow 3400 \rightarrow 6800$
8. $240 \leftarrow 480 \rightarrow 960$

## CFB ▪ 3a

1. $38 + 5 = 43$
$49 + 5 = 54$
$677 + 5 = 682$
$892 + 5 = 897$
$3246 + 5 = 3251$

2. $22 + 7 = 29$
$31 + 7 = 38$
$75 + 7 = 82$
$488 + 7 = 495$
$7095 + 7 = 7102$

3. $45 + 9 = 54$
$67 + 9 = 76$
$128 + 9 = 137$
$759 + 9 = 768$
$3244 + 9 = 3253$

## CFB ▪ 3b

$32 - 6 = 26$    $42 - 6 = 36$
$576 - 6 = 570$    $781 - 6 = 775$
$6455 - 6 = 6449$    $8004 - 6 = 7998$
$32 - 8 = 24$    $42 - 8 = 34$
$576 - 8 = 568$    $781 - 8 = 773$
$6455 - 8 = 6447$    $8004 - 8 = 7996$
$32 - 9 = 23$    $42 - 9 = 33$
$576 - 9 = 567$    $781 - 9 = 772$
$6455 - 9 = 6446$    $8004 - 9 = 7995$

## CFB ▪ 3c

**A** 1. 3 years    2. 368
3. 5 m    4. 5817
5. 7 km

**B**

| First stone | Second stone |
| --- | --- |
| 7 | 5 |
| 432 | 243 |
| 5 | 6 |
| 8651 | 6321 |
| 8 | 5 |

## CFB ▪ 4a

Children's answers may vary.

## CFB ▪ 4b

**A** 1. 85 mm    2. 45 mm
3. 125 mm    4. 120 mm
5. 50 mm    6. 135 mm

**B** 1. 20 mm    2. 30 mm
3. 45 mm    4. 35 mm
5. 15 mm    6. 25 mm

## CFB ▪ 5a

1. heptagon, regular
2. quadrilateral, regular
3. pentagon, irregular
4. hexagon, regular
5. quadrilateral, irregular
6. hexagon, irregular
7. hexagon, irregular
8. pentagon, irregular
9. triangle, irregular
10. triangle, irregular
11. pentagon, regular
12. octagon, irregular

13. triangle, regular
14. heptagon, irregular
15. quadrilateral, irregular
16. octagon, irregular
17. quadrilateral, irregular
18. heptagon, irregular

Children may choose different properties for each of these shapes.

## CFB ▪ 5b

 1, 2, 3, 6 and 7 are true reflections. 4, 5 and 8 are not true reflections.

| One line of symmetry | Two lines of symmetry | No lines of symmetry |
|---|---|---|
| 2, 5, 7, 9, 12 | 3, 8 | 1, 4, 6, 10, 11 |

## CFB ▪ 6

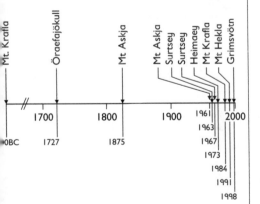

1. Children's answers may vary.
2. Children's answers may vary.
3. 30
4. No

## CFB ▪ 7a

1. never
2. always
3. always
4. never
5. always
6. sometimes
7. never

## CFB ▪ 7b

Children's answers may vary. The three templates below show the possible arrangements of odd (o) and even (e) numbers.

| e | o | e |
|---|---|---|
| o | o | o |
| e | o | e |

## CFB ▪ 8a

| | Number of stickers in each column | Number of stickers in each row | Total number of stickers |
|---|---|---|---|
| 1. | 5 | 6 | 30 |
| 2. | 6 | 2 | 12 |
| 3. | 6 | 4 | 24 |
| 4. | 4 | 10 | 40 |
| 5. | 5 | 8 | 40 |

| | Number of stickers in each column | Number of stickers in each row | Total number of stickers |
|---|---|---|---|
| 1. | 7 | 5 | 35 |
| 2. | 10 | 3 | 30 |
| 3. | 4 | 10 | 40 |
| 4. | 5 | 9 | 45 |
| 5. | 4 | 8 | 32 |

## CFB ■ 8b

| | | | |
|---|---|---|---|
| 1. | double 35 = 70 | 35 × 2 = 70 | 35 + 35 = 70 |
| 2. | double 36 = 72 | 36 × 2 = 72 | 36 + 36 = 72 |
| 3. | double 34 = 68 | 34 × 2 = 68 | 34 + 34 = 68 |
| 4. | double 40 = 80 | 40 × 2 = 80 | 40 + 40 = 80 |
| 5. | double 39 = 78 | 39 × 2 = 78 | 39 + 39 = 78 |
| 6. | double 48 = 96 | 48 × 2 = 96 | 48 + 48 = 96 |
| 7. | double 26 = 52 | 26 × 2 = 52 | 26 + 26 = 52 |
| 8. | double 54 = 108 | 54 × 2 = 108 | 54 + 54 = 108 |

## CFB ■ 8c

1. 3 → 6 → 12          3 × 4 = 12
2. 6 → 12 → 24        6 × 4 = 24
3. 4 → 8 → 16          4 × 4 = 16
4. 8 → 16 → 32        8 × 4 = 32
5. 7 → 14 → 28        7 × 4 = 28
6. 12 → 24 → 48      12 × 4 = 48
7. 23 → 46 → 92      23 × 4 = 92
8. 18 → 36 → 72      18 × 4 = 72
9. 25 → 50 → 100    25 × 4 = 100

## CFB ■ 9a

1.
| double | 23 | 46 |
|---|---|---|
| double | 230 | 460 |
| double | 2300 | 4600 |

2.
| double | 41 | 82 |
|---|---|---|
| double | 410 | 820 |
| double | 4100 | 8200 |

3.
| double | 37 | 74 |
|---|---|---|
| double | 370 | 740 |
| double | 3700 | 7400 |

4.
| double | 32 | 64 |
|---|---|---|
| double | 320 | 640 |
| double | 3200 | 6400 |

5.
| double | 28 | 56 |
|---|---|---|
| double | 280 | 560 |
| double | 2800 | 5600 |

6.
| double | 49 | 98 |
|---|---|---|
| double | 490 | 980 |
| double | 4900 | 9800 |

## CFB ■ 9b

**A**

1. 3 → 30 → 15          3 × 5 = 15
2. 5 → 50 → 25          5 × 5 = 25
3. 9 → 90 → 45          9 × 5 = 45
4. 6 → 60 → 30          6 × 5 = 30
5. 7 → 70 → 35          7 × 5 = 35
6. 14 → 140 → 70      14 × 5 = 70
7. 21 → 210 → 105    21 × 5 = 105
8. 17 → 170 → 85      17 × 5 = 85
9. 26 → 260 → 130    26 × 5 = 130

**B**

1. 4 → 40 → 80          4 × 20 = 80
2. 7 → 70 → 140        7 × 20 = 140
3. 8 → 80 → 160        8 × 20 = 160
4. 6 → 60 → 120        6 × 20 = 120
5. 5 → 50 → 100        5 × 20 = 100
6. 12 → 120 → 240    12 × 20 = 240
7. 24 → 240 → 480    24 × 20 = 480
8. 19 → 190 → 380    19 × 20 = 380
9. 27 → 270 → 540    27 × 20 = 540

## CFB ■ 9c

1.

2.

3.

4.
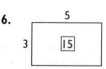

5.

6.

**7.**

**8.**

| | 5 |
|---|---|
| **4** | 20 |

**9.**

| | **6** |
|---|---|
| 3 | 18 |

## CFB ▪ 10a

**A** The children's sentences will vary but they should reflect these fractions:

1. blue = $\frac{1}{2}$, green = $\frac{1}{4}$, yellow = $\frac{1}{4}$

2. green = $\frac{1}{2}$, blue = $\frac{1}{4}$, yellow = $\frac{1}{4}$

3. green = $\frac{1}{2}$, yellow = $\frac{1}{4}$, blue = $\frac{1}{4}$

4. yellow = $\frac{1}{3}$, purple = $\frac{1}{6}$, green = $\frac{1}{6}$, blue = $\frac{1}{6}$, orange = $\frac{1}{6}$

5. orange = $\frac{1}{3}$, green = $\frac{1}{3}$, purple = $\frac{1}{3}$

6. red = $\frac{1}{4}$, blue = $\frac{1}{4}$, orange = $\frac{1}{4}$, yellow = $\frac{1}{4}$

7. blue = $\frac{1}{3}$, purple = $\frac{1}{3}$, green = $\frac{1}{6}$, yellow = $\frac{1}{6}$

8. purple = $\frac{1}{2}$, blue = $\frac{1}{5}$, orange = $\frac{1}{5}$, green = $\frac{1}{10}$

9. red = $\frac{9}{20}$, yellow = $\frac{3}{10}$, blue = $\frac{3}{20}$, orange = $\frac{1}{20}$, purple = $\frac{1}{20}$

10. purple = $\frac{1}{2}$, red = $\frac{1}{4}$, blue = $\frac{1}{4}$

**B**

1. red = $\frac{1}{2}$, blue = $\frac{1}{4}$, purple = $\frac{1}{4}$

2. purple = $\frac{1}{3}$, blue = $\frac{1}{3}$, red = $\frac{1}{3}$

3. purple = $\frac{1}{4}$, green = $\frac{1}{4}$, yellow = $\frac{1}{4}$, blue = $\frac{1}{4}$

4. orange = $\frac{1}{2}$, green = $\frac{1}{2}$

5. blue = $\frac{1}{3}$, yellow = $\frac{1}{3}$, red = $\frac{1}{6}$, purple = $\frac{1}{6}$

6. yellow = $\frac{1}{3}$, blue = $\frac{1}{6}$, green = $\frac{1}{6}$, orange = $\frac{1}{6}$, purple = $\frac{1}{6}$

7. green = $\frac{1}{3}$, purple = $\frac{1}{3}$, yellow = $\frac{1}{6}$, blue = $\frac{1}{6}$

8. yellow = $\frac{1}{2}$, blue = $\frac{3}{10}$, green = $\frac{1}{5}$

9. red = $\frac{2}{5}$, blue = $\frac{2}{5}$, yellow = $\frac{1}{5}$

10. blue = $\frac{1}{2}$, purple = $\frac{1}{4}$, yellow = $\frac{1}{8}$, red = $\frac{1}{8}$

## CFB ▪ 10b

**A** 1. $\frac{3}{4}$ of the shape is red.

   More than $\frac{1}{2}$ of the shape is red.

2. $\frac{1}{3}$ of the shape is red.

   Less than $\frac{1}{2}$ of the shape is red.

3. $\frac{5}{8}$ of the shape is red.

   More than $\frac{1}{2}$ of the shape is red.

4. $\frac{3}{8}$ of the shape is red.

   Less than $\frac{1}{2}$ of the shape is red.

**5.** $\frac{1}{6}$ of the shape is red.

Less than $\frac{1}{2}$ of the shape is red.

**6.** $\frac{2}{3}$ of the shape is red.

More than $\frac{1}{2}$ of the shape is red.

**7.** $\frac{1}{8}$ of the shape is red.

Less than $\frac{1}{2}$ of the shape is red.

**8.** $\frac{5}{6}$ of the shape is red.

More than $\frac{1}{2}$ of the shape is red.

**B** These fractions are more than $\frac{1}{2}$:

$\frac{5}{6}$   $\frac{5}{8}$   $\frac{7}{8}$   $\frac{2}{3}$   $\frac{3}{4}$

**C** Children's answers may vary.

## CFB ▪ 11a

**A** Children's answers may vary.

**B** watch a film → about 2 hours
boil a kettle → about 3 minutes
walk across the playground → about
30 seconds
mustard and cress sprout → about 2
days
a school term → about 3 months
summer holidays → about 6 weeks
time between Olympic games →
about 4 years

## CFB ▪ 11b

**1.**

21 minutes past 3

**2.**

2:02

2 minutes past 2

**3.**

6 minutes to 9

**4.**

10:36

24 minutes to 11

**5.**

1:16

16 minutes past 1

**6.**

12 minutes past 9

**7.**

9:37

23 minutes to 10

**8.**

18 minutes to 7

Children's sentences for times using a.m.
and p.m. will vary.

## CFB ▪ 11c

| Film starts | Film ends |
|---|---|
| 12:00 | 1:30 |
| 1:45 | 3:15 |
| 3:30 | 5:00 |
| 5:15 | 6:45 |
| 7:00 | 8:30 |

**B**

| Annie's Pantry | Goldrush Creek | | Fire Mountain | | Annie's Pantry |
|---|---|---|---|---|---|
| departs | arrives | departs | arrives | departs | arrives |
| 10:00 | 10:05 | 10:10 | 10:20 | 10:25 | 10:30 |
| 10:45 | 10:50 | 10:55 | 11:05 | 11:10 | 11:15 |
| 11:30 | 11:35 | 11:40 | 11:50 | 11:55 | 12:00* |
| 12:15* | 12:20* | 12:25* | 12:35* | 12:40* | 12:45* |

*These times are p.m.

## CFB ▪ 12

**A** Children's answers may vary. Here is some information about the graph:

The graph shows the number of pieces of litter on the school playground for each day of the week. There were 60 pieces of litter on Monday, 40 on Tuesday, 55 on Wednesday, 20 on Thursday and 10 on Friday. In total, there were 185 pieces of litter. Monday had the most litter and Friday had the least litter.

**B** Children's answers may vary. Here is some information about each of the graphs:

The bar chart shows the amount of rain that fell each day during the week. 2 mm fell on Tuesday, 8 mm fell on Thursday and 14 mm fell on Friday. No rain was recorded on any of the other days.

This table gives the number of pieces of each type of litter.

| | crisp packets | tissues | sweet papers | apple cores | drink cartons |
|---|---|---|---|---|---|
| Monday | 23 | 12 | 15 | 5 | 3 |
| Tuesday | 15 | 5 | 20 | 1 | 2 |
| Wednesday | 16 | 6 | 21 | 2 | 5 |
| Thursday | 6 | 2 | 11 | 0 | 0 |
| Friday | 2 | 2 | 6 | 0 | 0 |

The third graph shows the numbers of pieces of litter that were found at different times of the day. 15 pieces were dropped at 9:00 a.m., 10 at 11:00 a.m., 25 at 1:00 p.m., 5 at 3:00 p.m. and 10 at 5:00 p.m.

## CFB ▪ 13a

**Top cloud**

| Th | H | T | Ones | |
|---|---|---|---|---|
| | | | 2 | |
| | | 2 | 0 | 2 × 10 |
| | 2 | 0 | 0 | 2 × 100 |

| Th | H | T | Ones | |
|---|---|---|---|---|
| | | | 3 | |
| | | 3 | 0 | 3 × 10 |
| | 3 | 0 | 0 | 3 × 100 |

| Th | H | T | Ones | |
|---|---|---|---|---|
|  |  |  | 6 | |
|  |  | 6 | 0 | 6 × 10 |
|  | 6 | 0 | 0 | 6 × 100 |

| Th | H | T | Ones | |
|---|---|---|---|---|
|  |  |  | 8 | |
|  |  | 8 | 0 | 8 × 10 |
|  | 8 | 0 | 0 | 8 × 100 |

| Th | H | T | Ones | |
|---|---|---|---|---|
|  |  | 1 | 1 | |
|  | 1 | 1 | 0 | 11 × 10 |
| 1 | 1 | 0 | 0 | 11 × 100 |

| Th | H | T | Ones | |
|---|---|---|---|---|
|  |  | 3 | 4 | |
|  | 3 | 4 | 0 | 34 × 10 |
| 3 | 4 | 0 | 0 | 34 × 100 |

| Th | H | T | Ones | |
|---|---|---|---|---|
|  |  | 5 | 4 | |
|  | 5 | 4 | 0 | 54 × 10 |
| 5 | 4 | 0 | 0 | 54 × 100 |

| Th | H | T | Ones | |
|---|---|---|---|---|
|  |  | 6 | 7 | |
|  | 6 | 7 | 0 | 67 × 10 |
| 6 | 7 | 0 | 0 | 67 × 100 |

| Th | H | T | Ones | |
|---|---|---|---|---|
|  |  | 7 | 2 | |
|  | 7 | 2 | 0 | 72 × 10 |
| 7 | 2 | 0 | 0 | 72 × 100 |

| Th | H | T | Ones | |
|---|---|---|---|---|
|  |  | 9 | 9 | |
|  | 9 | 9 | 0 | 99 × 10 |
| 9 | 9 | 0 | 0 | 99 × 100 |

**Bottom cloud**

| Th | H | T | Ones | |
|---|---|---|---|---|
|  | 3 | 0 | 0 | |
|  |  | 3 | 0 | 300 ÷ 10 |
|  |  |  | 3 | 300 ÷ 100 |

| Th | H | T | Ones | |
|---|---|---|---|---|
|  | 7 | 0 | 0 | |
|  |  | 7 | 0 | 700 ÷ 10 |
|  |  |  | 7 | 700 ÷ 100 |

| Th | H | T | Ones | |
|---|---|---|---|---|
|  | 9 | 0 | 0 | |
|  |  | 9 | 0 | 900 ÷ 10 |
|  |  |  | 9 | 900 ÷ 100 |

| Th | H | T | Ones | |
|---|---|---|---|---|
| 1 | 0 | 0 | 0 | |
|  | 1 | 0 | 0 | 1000 ÷ 10 |
|  |  | 1 | 0 | 1000 ÷ 100 |

| Th | H | T | Ones | |
|---|---|---|---|---|
| 4 | 1 | 0 | 0 | |
|  | 4 | 1 | 0 | 4100 ÷ 10 |
|  |  | 4 | 1 | 4100 ÷ 100 |

| Th | H | T | Ones | |
|---|---|---|---|---|
| 5 | 2 | 0 | 0 | |
|  | 5 | 2 | 0 | 5200 ÷ 10 |
|  |  | 5 | 2 | 5200 ÷ 100 |

| Th | H | T | Ones | |
|---|---|---|---|---|
| 8 | 8 | 0 | 0 | |
|  | 8 | 8 | 0 | 8800 ÷ 10 |
|  |  | 8 | 8 | 8800 ÷ 100 |

| Th | H | T | Ones | |
|---|---|---|---|---|
| 9 | 0 | 0 | 0 | |
|  | 9 | 0 | 0 | 9000 ÷ 10 |
|  |  | 9 | 0 | 9000 ÷ 100 |

## CFB ▪ 13b

1. 75  　　2. 15  　　3. 200
4. 70  　　5. 400  　　6. 52

## CFB ▪ 13c

1. 60 cm  　　2. 60 kg  　　3. 200 ml
4. Five past 5  　　5. 350 kg  　　6. $27\frac{1}{2}$ cm

## CFB ▪ 14a

1.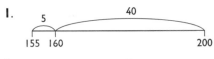

2.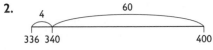

3.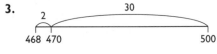

4.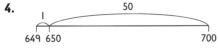

5.

## CFB ▪ 14b

1.

2.

3.

4.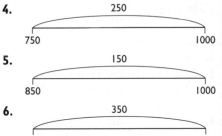

5.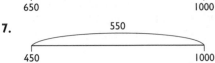

6.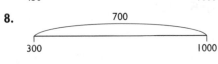

7.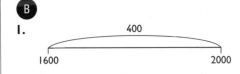

8.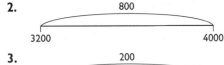

**B**

1.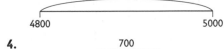

2.

3.

4.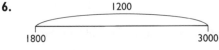

5.

6.

## CFB ▪ 15a

1. 36 + 14 = 50 and 34 + 16 = 50
2. 16 + 14 = 30
3. 23 + 17 = 40 and 13 + 27 = 40
4. 12 + 38 = 50 and 18 + 32 = 50
5. 34 + 26 = 60 and 36 + 24 = 60
6. 23 + 47 = 70 and 27 + 43 = 70
7. 48 + 32 = 80 and 42 + 38 = 80
8. 31 + 59 = 90 and 39 + 51 = 90
9. 47 + 53 = 100 and 43 + 57 = 100

## CFB ▪ 15b

1. Any pair of these numbers added together will give an even answer.

2. 15 + 23 = 38

3. 15 + 97 = 112;  23 + 83 = 106;
   23 + 97 = 120;  37 + 69 = 106;
   37 + 71 = 108;  37 + 83 = 120;
   37 + 97 = 134;  41 + 69 = 110;
   41 + 71 = 112;  41 + 83 = 124;
   41 + 97 = 138,  55 + 69 = 124;
   55 + 71 = 126;  55 + 83 = 138;
   55 + 97 = 152;  69 + 71 = 140;
   69 + 83 = 152;  69 + 97 = 166;
   71 + 83 = 154;  71 + 97 = 168;
   83 + 97 = 180

4. 15 + 23 = 38; 15 + 37 = 52;
   15 + 41 = 56; 23 + 37 = 60;
   23 + 41 = 64

5. 15 + 69 = 84; 15 + 71 = 86;
   23 + 55 = 78; 37 + 41 = 78

6. Not possible. Two odd numbers always have an even total.

7. 15 + 69 = 84; 23 + 37 = 60;
   23 + 55 = 78; 23 + 97 = 120;
   37 + 41 = 78; 37 + 71 = 108;
   37 + 83 = 120; 41 + 55 = 96;
   41 + 97 = 138; 55 + 71 = 126;
   71 + 97 = 168; 55 + 83 = 138;
   83 + 97 = 180

8. 83 + 97 = 180

## CFB ▪ 16a

Reasonable answers are:

A. Bathroom scales: suitcase, potatoes, oranges, apples
   Kitchen scales: apples, oranges, flour, rice
   Spring balance: strawberries, rice, flour
B. 10 litre bucket: wading pool
   2 litre measuring container: lemonade, teapot, vegetable oil
   500 ml cylinder: vegetable oil, shampoo, cough medicine, mug
   20 ml beaker: none (all items shown have capacities greater than 20 ml)

## CFB ▪ 16b

A. Lemonade: 1500 millilitres
   Orange juice: 1000 millilitres
   Mint flavouring: one tenth of a litre
   Cola: 2 litres
   Cherryade: three quarters of a litre
   Tomato sauce: half a litre
   Spring water: 5 litres
   Apple juice: quarter of a litre

B. Flour: 1000 grams
   Chews: one tenth of a kilogram
   Biscuits: quarter of a kilogram
   Potatoes: 4000 grams
   Sugar: half a kilogram
   Soap powder: 2 kilograms
   Bananas: 1500 grams
   Rice: three quarters of a kilogram

## CFB ▪ 17a

**A** 1. 5 cubes  2. 5 cubes
   3. 6 cubes  4. 6 cubes
   5. 6 cubes  6. 6 cubes

**B** 1. 5 cubes  2. 6 cubes
   3. 8 cubes  4. 5 cubes
   5. 6 cubes  6. 7 cubes

## CFB ▪ 17b

| Prisms | number of faces | number of vertices | number of edges |
|---|---|---|---|
| Triangular prism | 5 | 6 | 9 |
| Square prism (cuboid) | 6 | 8 | 12 |
| Pentagonal prism | 7 | 10 | 15 |
| Hexagonal prism | 8 | 12 | 18 |

**B**

| Pyramids | number of faces | number of vertices | number of edges |
|---|---|---|---|
| Triangular-based pyramid | 4 | 4 | 6 |
| Square-based pyramid | 5 | 5 | 8 |
| Pentagonal-based pyramid | 6 | 6 | 10 |
| Hexagonal-based pyramid | 7 | 7 | 12 |

## CFB ▪ 18

1. Chimpanzee: 340 cm
   Lion: 3 m
   Crocodile: 12 m
   Wolf: 200 cm
   Giant panda: 3 m
   Hippopotamus: 8 m
   Flying squirrel: 42 cm
   Koala: 120 cm

2. Koala + Flying squirrel: 11 kg 50 g
   Koala + Chimpanzee: 91 kg
   Koala + Giant panda: 131 kg
   Koala + Crocodile: 761 kg
   Koala + Wolf: 91 kg
   Koala + Hippopotamus: 1511 kg
   Koala + Lion: 211 kg

   Flying squirrel + Chimpanzee: 80 kg 50 g
   Flying squirrel + Giant panda: 120 kg 50 g
   Flying squirrel + Crocodile: 750 kg 50 g

Flying squirrel + Wolf: 80 kg 50 g
Flying squirrel + Hippopotamus:
1500 kg 50 g
Flying squirrel + Lion: 200 kg 50 g

Chimpanzee + Giant panda: 200 kg
Chimpanzee + Crocodile: 830 kg
Chimpanzee + Wolf: 160 kg
Chimpanzee + Hippopotamus: 1580 kg
Chimpanzee + Lion: 280 kg

Giant panda + Crocodile: 870 kg
Giant panda + Wolf: 200 kg
Giant panda + Hippopotamus: 1620 kg
Giant panda + Lion: 320 kg

Crocodile + Wolf: 830 kg
Crocodile + Hippopotamus: 2250 kg
Crocodile + Lion: 950 kg

Wolf + Hippopotamus: 1580 kg
Wolf + Lion: 280 kg

Hippopotamus + Lion: 1700 kg

Heaviest: 2250 kg (hippopotamus and
crocodile)
Lightest: 11 kg 50 g (koala and flying
squirrel)

**3.**

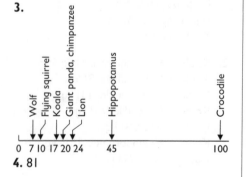

0   7 10 17 20 24    45                    100

**4.** 81

## CFB ■ 19a

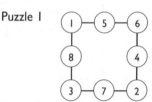

## CFB ■ 19b

Puzzle 1

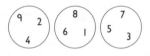

Puzzle 2 Possibilities include:

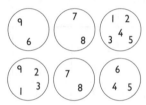

Puzzle 3
10

Puzzle 4
7 and 5, 20 and 4, 6 and 7

## CFB ■ 20a

**I.** $3 \times 4 = 12$    $12 \div 3 = 4$
$3 \times 5 = 15$    $15 \div 3 = 5$
$4 \times 4 = 16$    $16 \div 4 = 4$
$4 \times 5 = 20$    $20 \div 4 = 5$

**2.** $4 \times 3 = 12$    $12 \div 3 = 4$
$4 \times 4 = 16$    $16 \div 4 = 4$
$5 \times 3 = 15$    $15 \div 3 = 5$
$5 \times 4 = 20$    $20 \div 4 = 5$

**3.** $8 \times 4 = 32$    $32 \div 8 = 4$
    $8 \times 5 = 40$    $40 \div 8 = 5$
    $9 \times 4 = 36$    $36 \div 9 = 4$
    $9 \times 5 = 45$    $45 \div 9 = 5$

**4.** $9 \times 9 = 81$    $81 \div 9 = 9$
    $9 \times 10 = 90$    $90 \div 9 = 10$
    $10 \times 9 = 90$    $90 \div 10 = 9$
    $10 \times 10 = 100$    $100 \div 10 = 10$

**5.**

| 10 | 12 |
|----|----|
| 15 | 18 |

$2 \times 5 = 10$    $10 \div 2 = 5$
$2 \times 6 = 12$    $12 \div 2 = 6$
$3 \times 5 = 15$    $15 \div 3 = 5$
$3 \times 6 = 18$    $18 \div 3 = 6$

**6.**

| 45 | 54 |
|----|----|
| 50 | 60 |

$9 \times 5 = 45$    $45 \div 9 = 5$
$9 \times 6 = 54$    $54 \div 9 = 6$
$10 \times 5 = 50$    $50 \div 10 = 5$
$10 \times 6 = 60$    $60 \div 10 = 6$

**7.**

| 36 | 42 |
|----|----|
| 42 | 49 |

$6 \times 6 = 36$    $36 \div 6 = 6$
$6 \times 7 = 42$    $42 \div 6 = 7$
$7 \times 6 = 42$    $42 \div 7 = 6$
$7 \times 7 = 49$    $49 \div 7 = 7$

**8.**

| 25 | 30 |
|----|----|
| 30 | 36 |

$5 \times 5 = 25$    $25 \div 5 = 5$
$5 \times 6 = 30$    $30 \div 5 = 6$
$6 \times 5 = 30$    $30 \div 6 = 5$
$6 \times 6 = 36$    $36 \div 6 = 6$

## CFB ▪ 20b

**A**

**1.** $3 \rightarrow 12 \rightarrow 24$    $3 \times 8 = 24$
**2.** $6 \rightarrow 24 \rightarrow 48$    $6 \times 8 = 48$
**3.** $4 \rightarrow 16 \rightarrow 32$    $4 \times 8 = 32$
**4.** $8 \rightarrow 32 \rightarrow 64$    $8 \times 8 = 64$
**5.** $7 \rightarrow 28 \rightarrow 56$    $7 \times 8 = 56$
**6.** $11 \rightarrow 44 \rightarrow 88$    $11 \times 8 = 88$

**7.** $21 \rightarrow 84 \rightarrow 168$    $21 \times 8 = 168$
**8.** $12 \rightarrow 48 \rightarrow 96$    $12 \times 8 = 96$
**9.** $25 \rightarrow 100 \rightarrow 200$    $25 \times 8 = 200$

**B**

**1.** $3 \rightarrow 9 \rightarrow 18$    $3 \times 6 = 18$
**2.** $5 \rightarrow 15 \rightarrow 30$    $5 \times 6 = 30$
**3.** $9 \rightarrow 27 \rightarrow 54$    $9 \times 6 = 54$
**4.** $6 \rightarrow 18 \rightarrow 36$    $6 \times 6 = 36$
**5.** $7 \rightarrow 21 \rightarrow 42$    $7 \times 6 = 42$
**6.** $14 \rightarrow 42 \rightarrow 84$    $14 \times 6 = 84$
**7.** $21 \rightarrow 63 \rightarrow 126$    $21 \times 6 = 126$
**8.** $17 \rightarrow 51 \rightarrow 102$    $17 \times 6 = 102$
**9.** $26 \rightarrow 78 \rightarrow 156$    $26 \times 6 = 156$

## CFB ▪ 20c

**1.** $5 \boxed{\overset{11}{55}}$    $5 \times 11 = 55$

**2.** $7 \boxed{\overset{11}{77}}$    $7 \times 11 = 77$

**3.** $8 \boxed{\overset{11}{88}}$    $8 \times 11 = 88$

**4.** $4 \boxed{\overset{9}{36}}$    $4 \times 9 = 36$

**5.** $3 \boxed{\overset{9}{27}}$    $3 \times 9 = 27$

**6.** $5 \boxed{\overset{9}{45}}$    $5 \times 9 = 45$

**7.** $6 \boxed{\overset{11}{66}}$    $6 \times 11 = 66$

**8.** $9 \boxed{\overset{11}{99}}$    $9 \times 11 = 99$

## CFB ▪ 21a

**A**

1. $5 \times 8 = 25 + 15 = 40$

2. $5 \times 8 = 30 + 10 = 40$

3. $5 \times 8 = 20 + 20 = 40$

**B**

1.

| | 5 | 4 |
|---|---|---|
| 6 | 30 | 24 |

$6 \times 9 = 30 + 24 = 54$

2.

| | 5 | 1 |
|---|---|---|
| 7 | 35 | 7 |

$7 \times 6 = 35 + 7 = 42$

3.

| | 5 | 2 |
|---|---|---|
| 9 | 45 | 18 |

$9 \times 7 = 45 + 18 = 63$

4.

| | 6 | 3 |
|---|---|---|
| 6 | 36 | 18 |

$6 \times 9 = 36 + 18 = 54$

5.

| | 4 | 2 |
|---|---|---|
| 7 | 28 | 14 |

$7 \times 6 = 28 + 14 = 42$

6.

| | 4 | 3 |
|---|---|---|
| 9 | 36 | 27 |

$9 \times 7 = 36 + 27 = 63$

## CFB ▪ 21b

**A**
1. 120
2. 140
3. 90
4. 100
5. 160
6. 220

**B**

| Approximate answer | Calculation |
|---|---|
| 60 | $12 \times 6$, $14 \times 6$, $12 \times 7$ |
| 40 | $12 \times 4$, $14 \times 4$ |
| 80 | $12 \times 8$, $17 \times 4$, $22 \times 4$, $24 \times 4$, $14 \times 8$ |
| 140 | $22 \times 7$, $24 \times 7$, $17 \times 7$ |
| 120 | $17 \times 6$, $22 \times 6$, $24 \times 6$ |

## CFB ▪ 21c

1. Approximate answer: $6 \times 20 = 120$

| | 20 | 3 |
|---|---|---|
| 6 | $20 \times 6 = 120$ | $3 \times 6 = 18$ |

23

$120 + 18 = 138$
$6 \times 23 = 138$

2. Approximate answer: $4 \times 20 = 80$

| | 10 | 5 |
|---|---|---|
| 4 | $10 \times 4 = 40$ | $5 \times 4 = 20$ |

15

$40 + 20 = 60$
$4 \times 15 = 60$

**3.** Approximate answer: 8 × 10 = 80

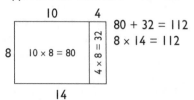

80 + 32 = 112
8 × 14 = 112

**4.** Approximate answer: 4 × 30 = 120

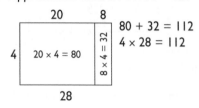

80 + 32 = 112
4 × 28 = 112

**5.** Approximate answer: 7 × 30 = 210

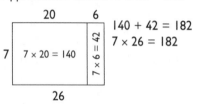

140 + 42 = 182
7 × 26 = 182

## CFB ▪ 22a

**1.**

**2.**

**3.**

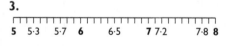

## CFB ▪ 22b

**1.** a → 0·2
b → 0·4
c → 0·5
d → 0·7
e → 0·9

**2.** a → 0·4
b → 0·9
c → 1·3
d → 1·6
e → 1·7

The following decimal fractions can be made using the numbers in the set:

3·2, 3·3, 3·7, 3·8, 5·2, 5·3, 5·7, 5·8, 7·2, 7·3, 7·7, 7·8, 9·2, 9·3, 9·7, 9·8

## CFB ▪ 22c

**1.** incorrect, correct, correct but incorrect logic
**2.** correct, incorrect, incorrect

**1.** 3·8      5·7      7·5      8·3      8·5
**2.** 4·6 m    5·8 m    6·4 m    6·8 m    8·4 m
**3.** 98 g     0·89 kg  980 g    1 kg     8·9 kg
**4.** 0·9 m    99 cm    1·9 m    199 cm   9 m

## CFB ▪ 23

Children's answers will vary depending on the questions asked.

## CFB ▪ 24a

The following should be vertical:
the lampshade, the grandfather clock, the flowers in the vase, the chair, the liquid poured from the bottle.

The following should be horizontal:
the liquid in the glass, the fish tank, the sofa, the window, the picture.

## CFB ▪ 24b

**a.** landing pad → (4,9)
**b.** giant crater → (2,7)
**c.** living pod → (3,4)
**d.** crash site → (8,8)

e. Xelg nursery → (9, 4)

f. undersea dome → (11,1)

## CFB ■ 24c

Children's answers may vary.

## CFB ■ 25a

Children's answers will vary according to the pairs of numbers chosen.

## CFB ■ 25b

### Electrical goods

| price | rounded to the nearest £10 | rounded to the nearest £100 |
|---|---|---|
| £379 | £380 | £400 |
| £148 | £150 | £100 |
| £175 | £180 | £200 |
| £203 | £200 | £200 |
| £119 | £120 | £100 |
| £189 | £190 | £200 |
| £227 | £230 | £200 |
| £455 | £460 | £500 |
| £244 | £240 | £200 |

### Ladders

| length | rounded to the nearest 10 cm | rounded to the nearest 100 cm |
|---|---|---|
| 297 cm | 300 cm | 300 cm |
| 714 cm | 710 cm | 700 cm |
| 185 cm | 190 cm | 200 cm |
| 234 cm | 230 cm | 200 cm |
| 104 cm | 100 cm | 100 cm |

### Cameras

| weight | rounded to the nearest 10 g | rounded to the nearest 100 g |
|---|---|---|
| 135 g | 140 g | 100 g |
| 155 g | 160 g | 200 g |
| 385 g | 390 g | 400 g |
| 265 g | 270 g | 300 g |
| 108 g | 110 g | 100 g |
| 784 g | 780 g | 800 g |

### Kitchen utensils

| capacity | rounded to the nearest 10 ml | rounded to the nearest 100 ml |
|---|---|---|
| 306 ml | 310 ml | 300 ml |
| 453 ml | 450 ml | 500 ml |
| 185 ml | 190 ml | 200 ml |
| 780 ml | 780 ml | 800 ml |
| 855 ml | 860 ml | 900 ml |

## CFB ■ 26a

| Food item | Amount eaten | | Total |
|---|---|---|---|
| | day 1 | day 2 | |
| raisins | 51 | 55 | 106 |
| peanuts | 59 | 43 | 102 |
| pumpkin seeds | 5 | 3 | 8 |
| sunflower seeds | 32 | 26 | 58 |

## CFB ■ 26b

Children's answers will vary. This table gives the cost of buying a bag each of two different foods.

|  | peanuts | raisins | millet | sunflower seeds | pumpkin seeds |
|---|---|---|---|---|---|
| peanuts |  | £6.94 | £4.08 | £8.44 | £7.24 |
| raisins | £6.94 |  | £4.12 | £8.48 | £7.28 |
| millet | £4.08 | £4.12 |  | £5.62 | £4.42 |
| sunflower seeds | £8.44 | £8.48 | £5.62 |  | £8.78 |
| pumpkin seeds | £7.24 | £7.28 | £4.42 | £8.78 |  |

## CFB ■ 27a

| | |
|---|---|
| 499 – 39 = 460 | 499 – 80 = 419 |
| 499 – 68 = 431 | 499 – 71 = 428 |
| 499 – 86 = 413 | 499 – 93 = 406 |
| | |
| 373 – 39 = 334 | 373 – 80 = 293 |
| 373 – 68 = 305 | 373 – 71 = 302 |
| 373 – 86 = 287 | 373 – 93 = 280 |
| | |
| 560 – 39 = 521 | 560 – 80 = 480 |
| 560 – 68 = 492 | 560 – 71 = 489 |
| 560 – 86 = 474 | 560 – 93 = 467 |
| | |
| 906 – 39 = 867 | 906 – 80 = 826 |
| 906 – 68 = 838 | 906 – 71 = 835 |
| 906 – 86 = 820 | 906 – 93 = 813 |
| | |
| 800 – 39 = 761 | 800 – 80 = 720 |
| 800 – 68 = 732 | 800 – 71 = 729 |
| 800 – 86 = 714 | 800 – 93 = 707 |
| | |
| 674 – 39 = 635 | 674 – 80 = 594 |
| 674 – 68 = 606 | 674 – 71 = 603 |
| 674 – 86 = 588 | 674 – 93 = 581 |

## CFB ■ 27b

Children's answers may vary.

## CFB ■ 28a

1. 24 cm    2. 16 cm
3. 14 cm    4. 29 cm
5. 12 cm    6. 10 cm

## CFB ■ 28b

1. 25    2. 28    3. 27    4. $23\frac{1}{2}$

## CFB ■ 29a

Children's answers will vary depending on the questions.

## CFB ■ 29b

1. 30°    2. 45°    3. 90°
4. 60°    5. 45°    6. 30°
7. 30°    8. 60°    9. 30°
10. 60°    11. 45°    12. 90°

## CFB ■ 30a

1–2 Answers on page.

3. 
| 10 | |
|---|---|
| 4 | 6 |

4. 
| 18 | | |
|---|---|---|
| 7 | 11 | |
| 3 | 4 | 7 |

5. 
| 140 | | | |
|---|---|---|---|
| 60 | 80 | | |
| 25 | 35 | 45 | |
| 10 | 15 | 20 | 25 |

6. 
| 14 | |
|---|---|
| 3 | 11 |

7. 
| 9 | | |
|---|---|---|
| 4 | 5 | |
| 2 | 2 | 3 |

8. 
| 60 | | | |
|---|---|---|---|
| 27 | 33 | | |
| 12 | 15 | 18 | |
| 5 | 7 | 8 | 10 |

## CFB ▪ 30b

**1.** 174    **2.** 55     **3.** 75
**4.** Girl-Gang (164 CDs)

## CFB ▪ 31a

**1.** always      **2.** sometimes
**3.** always      **4.** never
**5.** always      **6.** always
**7.** always

## CFB ▪ 31b

**1.** $2n - 1$ (add 2 each time)

| Shape number | 1 | 2 | 3 | 4 | 10 |
|---|---|---|---|---|---|
| Number of squares | 1 | 3 | 5 | 7 | 19 |

**2.** $3n + 1$ (add 3 each time)

| Shape number | 1 | 2 | 3 | 10 |
|---|---|---|---|---|
| Number of matches | 4 | 7 | 10 | 31 |

**3.** $2n + 1$ (add 2 each time)

| Shape number | 1 | 2 | 3 | 10 |
|---|---|---|---|---|
| Number of matches | 3 | 5 | 7 | 21 |

**4.** $3n - 2$ (add 3 each time)

| Shape number | 1 | 2 | 3 | 4 | 10 |
|---|---|---|---|---|---|
| Number of squares | 1 | 4 | 7 | 10 | 28 |

## CFB ▪ 32a

**Page 1**
**1.** $7 \times 2 = 14$      **2.** $5 \times 3 = 15$
**3.** $8 \times 4 = 32$      **4.** $15 \times 2 = 30$
**5.** $5 \times 8 = 40$      **6.** $10 \times 7 = 70$
**7.** $9 \times 5 = 45$      **8.** $6 \times 4 = 24$

**Page 2**
**1.** $18 \div 2 = 9$      **2.** $24 \div 4 = 6$
**3.** $50 \div 5 = 10$      **4.** $24 \div 2 = 12$
**5.** $18 \div 3 = 6$      **6.** $80 \div 10 = 8$
**7.** $45 \div 5 = 9$      **8.** $240 \div 2 = 120$

## CFB ▪ 32b

**Left-hand side**
**1.** 78      **2.** 92      **3.** 114
**4.** 176      **5.** 90

Approximate answers:
**1.** $30 \times 3 = 90$      **2.** $20 \times 4 = 80$
**3.** $20 \times 6 = 120$      **4.** $20 \times 8 = 160$
**5.** $20 \times 5 = 100$

**Right-hand side**
**1.** 100      **2.** 136      **3.** 116
**4.** 54      **5.** 120

Approximate answers:
**1.** $30 \times 4 = 120$      **2.** $20 \times 8 = 160$
**3.** $30 \times 4 = 120$      **4.** $20 \times 3 = 60$
**5.** $20 \times 5 = 100$

## CFB ▪ 32c

**A**

**1.** 385      **2.** 72      **3.** 4800
**4.** 100      **5.** 1200      **6.** 81

**B**

**1.** 125      **2.** 75      **3.** 148
**4.** 245      **5.** 760      **6.** 286
**7.** 290      **8.** 438      **9.** 99
**10.** 392    **11.** 100    **12.** 93
**13.** 152    **14.** 195    **15.** 850
**16.** 234    **17.** 264    **18.** 656
**19.** 88      **20.** 900

## CFB ▪ 33a

1. 20 r3   2. 40   3. 23
4. 26   5. 19 r2   6. 31 r3

## CFB ▪ 33b

1. £5.50   2. £3.50   3. £12.50
4. £9.40   5. £10.75

**B**

1. 7 bags   2. 8 packets
3. 14 trays   4. £3.25
5. one

## CFB ▪ 34a

Possible answers include:
1. 1 yellow tile for every 2 red tiles
2. 1 blue bead for every 3 green beads
3. 1 filling for every 2 pieces of bread
4. 5 toes for every foot
   *or* 1 left leg for every right leg
   *or* 2 feet for every person
5. 6 fish for every penguin
   *or* 2 eyes for every beak
6. 3 wheels for every tricycle
   *or* 2 handlebars for every tricycle
   *or* 2 pedals for every tricycle
   *or* 1 big wheel for every 2 small wheels
7. 6 strawberries for every cake
8. 1 lamp post for every 4 houses
   *or* 1 door (or roof) for every house

## CFB ▪ 34b

1. $\frac{1}{4}$ bottle of cola each

2. $\frac{2}{3}$ bun each

3. $1\frac{1}{2}$ pizzas each

4. 3 apples each

5. £2.50 each

## CFB ▪ 35a

1. 14   2. 20   3. 40

## CFB ▪ 35b

1. £7.20 altogether   2. £2.50 left
3. No (£10.02 for all three)

## CFB ▪ 35c

1. 20 buckets   2. 5 snakes
3. 72 m

## CFB ▪ 36a

Children's answers may vary.

## CFB ▪ 36b

**A**

1.

| Film starts | Length of film | Film ends | Interval between films |
|---|---|---|---|
| 2:10 p.m. | 1 hour 30 mins | 3:40 p.m. | 40 mins |
| 4:20 p.m. | 1 hour 30 mins | 5:50 p.m. | |

2.

| Ticket prices | |
|---|---|
| Adult | £3.25 |
| Child | £2.00 |
| Over 60s | £1.50 |

 **B**   Children's answers may vary.

## Practice ▪ 1a

**①** 1. 11 2. 13 3. 34
4. 60 5. 36 6. 100
7. 8 8. 2 9. 80

**②** Horizontally:
3 + 4 = 7  4 + 5 = 9  1 + 2 = 3
2 + 3 = 5  5 + 2 = 7  2 + 6 = 8

Vertically:
3 + 1 = 4  1 + 5 = 6  4 + 2 = 6
2 + 2 = 4  5 + 3 = 8  3 + 6 = 9

**③** 1. 7 2. 5 3. 6
4. 8 5. 28 6. 49

**④**

| | | | | | | | 116 | |
|---|---|---|---|---|---|---|---|---|
| | 31 | | | 74 | | | 60 | 56 |
| 15 | 16 | | 36 | 38 | | 31 | 29 | 27 |
| 8 | 7 | 9 | 21 | 15 | 23 | 16 | 15 | 14 | 13 |

**⑤** Children should realize that multiplying by 10 twice is the same as multiplying by 100.

6 → 60 → 600
6 → 600

16 → 160 → 1600
16 → 1600

34 → 340 → 3400
34 → 3400

40 → 400 → 4000
40 → 4000

81 → 810 → 8100
81 → 8100

98 → 980 → 9800
98 → 9800

## Practice ▪ 1b

**①** 1. 20 2. 10 3. 8
4. 20 5. 16 6. 5
7. 2 8. 7 9. 6

**②**

| − | 5 | 9 |
|---|---|---|
| 4 | 1 | 5 |
| 2 | 3 | 7 |

| − | 8 | 6 |
|---|---|---|
| 3 | 5 | 3 |
| 5 | 3 | 1 |

| − | 7 | 4 |
|---|---|---|
| 4 | 3 | 0 |
| 2 | 5 | 2 |

| − | 9 | 8 |
|---|---|---|
| 7 | 2 | 1 |
| 5 | 4 | 3 |

| − | 7 | 6 |
|---|---|---|
| 6 | 1 | 0 |
| 1 | 6 | 5 |

**③**

| 10 more | 25 | 59 | 510 | 200 | 1010 | 42 | 241 | 718 | 107 |
|---|---|---|---|---|---|---|---|---|---|
| number | 15 | 49 | 500 | 190 | 1000 | 32 | 231 | 708 | 97 |
| 10 less | 5 | 39 | 490 | 180 | 990 | 22 | 221 | 698 | 87 |

**④** Children's answers may vary.

**⑤** 18  17  27

## Practice ▪ 2a

**①** 1. 11 2. 7 3. 70
4. 29 5. 24 6. 8
7. 479 8. 713 9. 6

**②** Any of the following:

23 + 13 = 36   45 + 13 = 58
23 + 31 = 54   45 + 31 = 76
23 + 23 = 46   45 + 23 = 68
23 + 42 = 65   45 + 42 = 87
23 + 14 = 37   45 + 14 = 59

32 + 13 = 45   51 + 13 = 64
32 + 31 = 63   51 + 31 = 82
32 + 23 = 55   51 + 23 = 74
32 + 42 = 74   51 + 42 = 93
32 + 14 = 46   51 + 14 = 65

14 + 13 = 27
14 + 31 = 45
14 + 23 = 37
14 + 42 = 56
14 + 14 = 28

**3**

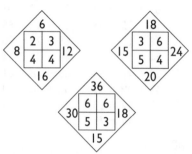

**4**  9 cm

**5**  Any of the following:

$$\frac{2}{5} \quad \frac{2}{4} \quad \frac{2}{3} \quad \frac{2}{10} \quad \frac{1}{2} \quad \frac{1}{5} \quad \frac{1}{4} \quad \frac{1}{3}$$

$$\frac{1}{10} \quad \frac{4}{5} \quad \frac{4}{10} \quad \frac{3}{5} \quad \frac{3}{4} \quad \frac{3}{10} \quad \frac{5}{10}$$

## Practice ▪ 2b

**1**  1. 5  2. 1  3. 11
    4. 5  5. 3  6. 8
    7. 5  8. 20  9. 100

**2**

| 20 | 100 | 420 | 50 | 900 | 30 | 170 | 550 |
|----|-----|-----|----|-----|----|-----|-----|
| 2  | 10  | 42  | 5  | 90  | 3  | 17  | 55  |

**3**  Children's answers may vary.

**4**  2 × 3 = 12 ÷ 2    9 × 1 = 36 ÷ 4
    5 × 4 = 100 ÷ 5    7 × 2 = 28 ÷ 2
    4 × 3 = 36 ÷ 3

**5**  Children's answers may vary
    between maximum of £5 and
    minimum of £1.02.

## Practice ▪ 3a

**1**  1. 36  2. 8  3. 175
    4. 899  5. 137  6. 450
    7. 192  8. 437  9. 7

**2**

| − | 37 | 59 |
|----|----|----|
| 16 | 21 | 43 |
| 24 | 13 | 35 |

| − | 86 | 28 |
|----|----|----|
| 15 | 71 | 13 |
| 23 | 63 | 5 |

| − | 99 | 78 |
|----|----|----|
| 46 | 53 | 32 |
| 57 | 42 | 21 |

| − | 74 | 85 |
|----|----|----|
| 31 | 43 | 54 |
| 62 | 12 | 23 |

**3**  Children's answers may vary.

**4**

| 90 | 80 | 80 | 10 |
|----|----|----|----|
| 90 | 70 | 60 | 30 |
| 90 | 60 | 40 | 50 |

**5**  Any of these calculations or these
    calculations reversed:

    34 + 24 = 58    34 + 43 = 77
    26 + 43 = 69    62 + 24 = 86
                    or 43 + 43 = 86

## Practice ▪ 3b

**1**  1. 5  2. 7  3. 24
    4. 500  5. 8  6. 27
    7. 10  8. 50  9. 400

**2**  1. 5 cm  2. 3 cm  3. 2 cm
    4. 9 cm  5. 13 cm

**3** Any of the following:

| | |
|---|---|
| 21 + 42 = 63 | 21 + 54 = 75 |
| 21 + 33 = 54 | 21 + 65 = 86 |

| | |
|---|---|
| 14 + 42 = 56 | 14 + 54 = 68 |
| 14 + 33 = 47 | 14 + 65 = 79 |

| | |
|---|---|
| 32 + 42 = 74 | 32 + 54 = 86 |
| 32 + 33 = 65 | 32 + 65 = 97 |

**4** Any of the following:

| | |
|---|---|
| 2 × 3 = 6 | 2 × 4 = 8 |
| 2 × 5 = 10 | 2 × 6 = 12 |
| 2 × 10 = 20 | |
| 3 × 4 = 12 | 3 × 5 = 15 |
| 3 × 6 = 18 | 3 × 10 = 30 |
| 4 × 5 = 20 | 4 × 6 = 24 |
| 4 × 10 = 40 | |
| 5 × 6 = 30 | 5 × 10 = 50 |
| 6 × 10 = 60 | |

**5** Children's answers may vary. Here is one example:

2   5   8   11   14   17

## Practice ■ 4a

**1** 1. 130   2. 1000   3. 21
4. 20   5. 52   6. 122
7. 8   8. 70   9. 800

**2** Any of the following:

| | |
|---|---|
| 18 ÷ 3 = 6 | 60 ÷ 10 = 6 |
| 20 ÷ 4 = 5 | 20 ÷ 5 = 4 |
| 24 ÷ 4 = 6 | 24 ÷ 6 = 4 |

**3** 17 → 34 → 68   17 × 4 = 68
30 → 60 → 120   30 × 4 = 120
25 → 50 → 100   25 × 4 = 100

**4** Any six of the following:

| | |
|---|---|
| 24 + 29 = 53 | 24 + 49 = 73 |
| 47 + 26 = 73 | 24 + 17 = 41 |
| 47 + 18 = 65 | 47 + 44 = 91 |
| 65 + 26 = 91 | 74 + 17 = 91 |
| 16 + 25 = 41 | 16 + 49 = 65 |
| 28 + 25 = 53 | 65 + 25 = 90 |
| 74 + 18 = 92 | 16 + 38 = 54 |
| 28 + 26 = 54 | 43 + 18 = 61 |
| 43 + 49 = 92 | 52 + 38 = 90 |
| 37 + 17 = 54 | 29 + 25 = 54 |
| 29 + 44 = 73 | |

**5** Children's answers may vary, e.g., 153 < 214 < 287 < 693.

## Practice ■ 4b

**1** 1. 7   2. 3   3. 90
4. 37   5. 100   6. 150
7. 11   8. 30   9. 37

**2** Children's answers may vary. Check that their triangles meet the requirements stated.

**3** Any of the following:

| | |
|---|---|
| 26 + 57 = 83 | 27 + 56 = 83 |
| 26 + 58 = 84 | 27 + 58 = 85 |
| 26 + 59 = 85 | 27 + 59 = 86 |

| | |
|---|---|
| 28 + 56 = 84 | 29 + 58 = 87 |
| 28 + 57 = 85 | 29 + 57 = 86 |
| 28 + 59 = 87 | 29 + 56 = 85 |

**4** Any of the following:

$47 - 31 = 16$  $69 - 31 = 38$
$47 - 22 = 25$  $69 - 22 = 47$
$47 - 15 = 32$  $69 - 15 = 54$

$56 - 31 = 25$  $88 - 31 = 57$
$56 - 22 = 34$  $88 - 22 = 66$
$56 - 15 = 41$  $88 - 15 = 73$

$79 - 31 = 48$
$79 - 22 = 57$
$79 - 15 = 64$

**5** **1.** 84  101  203  11  462  310
**2.** 120  1004  107  199  990  200

## Practice ■ 5a

**1** **1.** 15   **2.** 50   **3.** 800
**4.** 40   **5.** 150   **6.** 4
**7.** 53   **8.** 194   **9.** 103

**2** **1.** 14   **2.** 40   **3.** 10
**4.** 80   **5.** 2   **6.** 10

**3** **1.** 57 stickers   **2.** 20 children
**3.** 50 feet

**4** Any of the following:

$567 + 8 = 575$    $567 + 9 = 576$
$576 + 8 = 584$    $576 + 9 = 585$
$657 + 8 = 665$    $657 + 9 = 666$
$675 + 8 = 683$    $675 + 9 = 684$
$756 + 8 = 764$    $756 + 9 = 765$
$765 + 8 = 773$    $765 + 9 = 774$

**5** $213 \rightarrow 212 \rightarrow 202 \rightarrow 102$
$480 \rightarrow 380 \rightarrow 379 \rightarrow 369$
$306 \rightarrow 296 \rightarrow 196 \rightarrow 195$

## Practice 5b

**1** **1.** 9   **2.** 20   **3.** 4
**4.** 9   **5.** 282   **6.** 73
**7.** 100   **8.** 8   **9.** 6

**2** **1.** £1.46   **2.** £2.50
**3.** £4.00   **4.** £6.03
**5.** £72.40   **6.** £10.00
**7.** £0.82   **8.** £0.05

**3** 1·5 litres = 1500 ml
4·1 litres = 4100 ml
1 litre = 1000 ml

7·3 litres = 7300 ml
3 litres = 3000 ml
0·3 litres = 300 ml

**4**

| ÷ | 10 | 20 |
|---|----|----|
| 2 | 5  | 10 |
| 5 | 2  | 4  |

| ÷ | 12 | 36 |
|---|----|----|
| 3 | 4  | 12 |
| 4 | 3  | 9  |

| ÷ | 18 | 24 |
|---|----|----|
| 2 | 9  | 12 |
| 3 | 6  | 8  |

| ÷ | 30 | 60 |
|---|----|----|
| 5 | 6  | 12 |
| 6 | 5  | 10 |

| ÷ | 16 | 28 |
|---|----|----|
| 4 | 4  | 7  |
| 2 | 8  | 14 |

**5** Any three of the following:

$256 + 78 = 334$  $267 + 58 = 325$
$256 + 87 = 343$  $267 + 85 = 352$
$265 + 78 = 343$  $276 + 58 = 334$
$265 + 87 = 352$  $276 + 85 = 361$
$257 + 68 = 325$  $268 + 57 = 325$
$257 + 86 = 343$  $268 + 75 = 343$
$275 + 68 = 343$  $286 + 57 = 343$
$275 + 86 = 361$  $286 + 75 = 361$
$258 + 67 = 325$  $278 + 56 = 334$
$258 + 76 = 334$  $278 + 65 = 343$
$285 + 67 = 352$  $287 + 56 = 343$
$285 + 76 = 361$  $287 + 65 = 352$

## Practice 6a

**1** 1. 60    2. 7    3. 284
4. 326    5. 37    6. 7
7. 90    8. 133    9. 87

**2** a 600 ml     b 800 ml
c 900 ml     d 300 ml

**3** £2.31    £1.78    £2.00
£3.02    £10.00

**4** Children's answers will vary.

**5** 1. 5    2. 9    3. 5
4. 10    5. 4    6. 6

## Practice ▪ 6b

**1** 1. 4    2. 9    3. 40
4. 74    5. 40    6. 50
7. 9    8. 91    9. 23

**2** 1. £50    2. 8    3. £375

**3** 1. 243    2. 468    3. 307
4. 558    5. 135    6. 609

**4** 1. 4    2. 2
3. 3    4. 3

**5** 64 + 75 **or** 74 + 65 = 139
64 − 57 = 7

## Practice ▪ 7a

**1** 1. 100    2. 40    3. 6
4. 45    5. 130    6. 300
7. 9    8. 17    9. 500

**2** Children's answers may vary.

**3** 1. 4 40 400     2. 6 60 600
3. 14 140 1400    4. 10 100 1000

**4** Any eight of the following:

3000 + 2 = 3002
3000 + 5 = 3005
3000 + 7 = 3007
800 + 2 = 802
800 + 5 = 805
800 + 7 = 807
6000 + 2 = 6002
6000 + 5 = 6005
6000 + 7 = 6007
9004 + 2 = 9006
9004 + 5 = 9009
9004 + 7 = 9011

**5** 406 − 399 = 7    405 − 398 = 7
404 − 397 = 7    403 − 396 = 7
402 − 395 = 7    401 − 394 = 7
400 − 393 = 7

## Practice ▪ 7b

**1** 1. 24    2. 8    3. 10
4. 13    5. 2    6. 80
7. 60    8. 100    9. 2

**2** 3 + 3 = 6     30 + 30 = 60
300 + 300 = 600

7 + 7 = 14     70 + 70 = 140
700 + 700 = 1400

12 + 12 = 24    120 + 120 = 240
1200 + 1200 = 2400

**3** 1. + ÷    2. − ×
3. × +    4. × −

**4** Any of the following, written out in words and figures:

4307 4370 4037 4073 4703 4730
3047 3074 3470 3407 3704 3740
7304 7340 7403 7430 7034 7043

**5** | $2 + 5 = 7$<br>$7 - 2 = 5$ | $20 + 50 = 70$<br>$70 - 20 = 50$

$200 + 500 = 700$
$700 - 200 = 500$

$2000 + 5000 = 7000$
$7000 - 2000 = 5000$

$20\,000 + 50\,000 = 70\,000$
$70\,000 - 20\,000 = 50\,000$

## Practice ▪ 8a

**1** | **1.** 19 | **2.** 70 | **3.** 110
**4.** 117 | **5.** 300 | **6.** 1300
**7.** 5 | **8.** 150 | **9.** 846

**2**

| + | 4 | 5 |
|---|---|---|
| 13 | 17 | 18 |
| 15 | 19 | 20 |

| + | 7 | 8 |
|---|---|---|
| 9 | 16 | 17 |
| 6 | 13 | 14 |

| + | 4 | 3 |
|---|---|---|
| 8 | 12 | 11 |
| 12 | 16 | 15 |

| + | 6 | 2 |
|---|---|---|
| 11 | 17 | 13 |
| 9 | 15 | 11 |

Children's answers may vary for the last grid. Here is one example.

| + | 10 | 6 |
|---|---|---|
| 5 | 15 | 11 |
| 8 | 18 | 14 |

**3** | 111, 211   404, 504   250, 350
39, 139   858, 758   537, 437
700, 600

**4** | **1.** $93 + 48 = 141$
**2.** $56 + 27 = 83$
**3.** $480 + 230 = 710$
**4.** $114 + 76 = 190$
**5.** $128 + 36 = 164$
**6.** $640 + 510 = 1150$

**5** | **1.** $46 \rightarrow 47$    **2.** $92 \rightarrow 91$
**3.** $76 \rightarrow 76$    **4.** $380 \rightarrow 370$

## Practice ▪ 8b

**1** | **1.** 60 | **2.** 40 | **3.** 600
**4.** 65 | **5.** 10 | **6.** 73
**7.** 8 | **8.** 7 | **9.** 93

**2** | **1.** wrong | **2.** wrong
**3.** correct | **4.** wrong

**3**

| − | 17 | 12 |
|---|---|---|
| 8 | 9 | 4 |
| 11 | 6 | 1 |

| − | 15 | 19 |
|---|---|---|
| 14 | 1 | 5 |
| 7 | 8 | 12 |

| − | 13 | 16 |
|---|---|---|
| 9 | 4 | 7 |
| 12 | 1 | 4 |

| − | 18 | 14 |
|---|---|---|
| 6 | 12 | 8 |
| 12 | 6 | 2 |

Children's answers may vary for the last grid. Here is one example.

| − | 14 | 22 |
|---|---|---|
| 6 | 8 | 16 |
| 8 | 6 | 14 |

**4** Children's answers may vary.

**5**

Children's answers may vary for the third triangle.

## Practice ▪ 9a

**1** | **1.** 24 | **2.** 6 | **3.** 3
**4.** 27 | **5.** 7 | **6.** 120
**7.** 16 | **8.** 150 | **9.** 3800

**2** | 203, 197   701, 695   402, 396
505, 499   604, 598

**3** | **1.** 4076 | **2.** 856 | **3.** 2898
**4.** 3276 | **5.** 503 | **6.** 716

**4** **1.** wrong **2.** correct
**3.** correct **4.** wrong

**5** Children's answers may vary.

## Practice ▪ 9b

**1** **1.** 25 **2.** 1 **3.** 15
**4.** 401 **5.** 2002 **6.** 30
**7.** 53 **8.** 8 **9.** 2

**2** 1224, 2224    1424, 2424
1443, 2443    1234, 2234
1334, 2334    1324, 2324

**3** **1.** 4 **2.** 6 **3.** 4 **4.** 9
**5.** 8 **6.** 9 **7.** 5 **8.** 5

**4** 2 m = 200 cm = 2000 mm
3 m = 300 cm = 3000 mm
5 m = 500 cm = 5000 mm
7 m = 700 cm = 7000 mm
8 m = 800 cm = 8000 mm

**5** Children's answers may vary.

## Practice ▪ 10a

**1** **1.** 14 **2.** 993 **3.** 8
**4.** 8 **5.** 6 **6.** 6999
**7.** 400 **8.** 900 **9.** 40

**2**

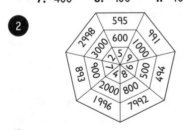

**3** Children's answers may vary.

**4** **1.** 5280   4280   3280   2280   1280
**2.** 9025   8025   7025   6025   5025
**3.** 6147   5147   4147   3147   2147

**5** Children's answers may vary.

## Practice ▪ 10b

**1** **1.** 300 **2.** 9 **3.** 10
**4.** 9 **5.** 17 **6.** 7
**7.** 30 **8.** 17 **9.** 80

**2** **1.** 63 **2.** 67 **3.** 68
**4.** 17 **5.** 91 **6.** 18

**3** Children's answers may vary.

**4** Any of the following:

| | |
|---|---|
| $142 - 6 = 136$ | $7106 - 6 = 7100$ |
| $8495 - 6 = 8489$ | $503 - 6 = 497$ |
| $142 - 7 = 135$ | $7106 - 7 = 7099$ |
| $8495 - 7 = 8488$ | $503 - 7 = 496$ |
| $142 - 8 = 134$ | $7106 - 8 = 7098$ |
| $8495 - 8 = 8487$ | $503 - 8 = 495$ |
| $142 - 9 = 133$ | $7106 - 9 = 7097$ |
| $8495 - 9 = 8486$ | $503 - 9 = 494$ |

**5** Children's answers may vary from
£1.04 to £9.

## Practice ▪ 11a

**1** **1.** 9 **2.** 17 **3.** 48
**4.** 3 **5.** 6002 **6.** 0
**7.** 34 **8.** 111 **9.** 422

**2**

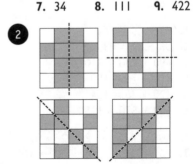

**3**
1. shorter than I metre
2. about I metre
3. shorter than I metre
4. shorter than I metre
5. longer than I metre
6. longer than I metre
7. about I metre
8. shorter than I metre
9. shorter than I metre

**4**
1. 15 19 23 27 31 35 39 43
2. 8 14 20 26 32 38 44 50
3. 10 17 24 31 38 45 52 59

**5** Children's answers may vary.

## Practice I Ib

**1**
| 1. 33 | 2. 10 | 3. 17 |
| 4. 600 | 5. 5 | 6. 15 |
| 7. 6004 | 8. 40 | 9. 9 |

**2**
$\frac{3}{4}$ m = 750 mm    $\frac{1}{2}$ m = 500 mm

$\frac{1}{4}$ m = 250 mm    $\frac{1}{10}$ m = 100 mm

$\frac{1}{2}$ km = 500 m    $\frac{3}{4}$ km = 750 m

$\frac{1}{4}$ km = 250 m

**3**
37   137   237   337   437
537   637   737   837

304   404   504   604   704
804   904   1004   1104

**4** 1. 25   2. 100   3. 80   4. 20

**5** Details may include:
triangle: 3 equal sides (equilateral)
quadrilateral: 2 right angles,
I pair parallel sides (trapezium)
quadrilateral: 2 pairs parallel sides,
no right angles (parallelogram)
pentagon: 3 right angles,
I pair parallel sides

## Practice ▪ 12a

**1**
| 1. 2 | 2. 592 | 3. 160 |
| 4. 28 | 5. 9 | 6. 3605 |
| 7. 130 | 8. 12 | 9. 8 |

**2**
1. 18   15   12   9   6   3   0
2. 32   27   22   17   12   7   2
3. 50   42   34   26   18   10   2

**3**
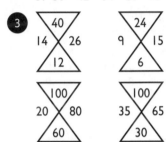

**4**
| 20 + 21 = 41 | 17 + 18 = 35 |
| 21 + 22 = 43 | 18 + 19 = 37 |
| 22 + 23 = 45 | 19 + 20 = 39 |

34 + 35 = 69
35 + 36 = 71
36 + 37 = 73

For each pattern, the answers
increase by 2.

**5** Children may find different ways
of organizing the sets. These have
been arranged according to the
numbers in the first circles.

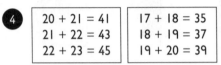

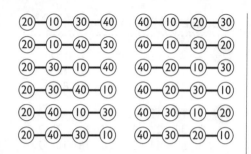

The third grid can give various answers, e.g.,

| × | 4 | 3 | 5 |
|---|---|---|---|
| 2 | 8 | 6 | 10 |
| 8 | 32 | 24 | 40 |

| × | 5 | 4 | 2 |
|---|---|---|---|
| 7 | 35 | 28 | 14 |
| 6 | 30 | 24 | 12 |

**3**  **1.** 95 stickers  **2.** 15 passengers
**3.** 40 choc-ices  **4.** 5 sweets

**4**

| Grid | Number of squares in each column | Number of squares in each row | Total number of squares |
|------|------|------|------|
| 3 × 6 | 3 | 6 | 18 |
| 2 × 5 | 2 | 5 | 10 |
| 4 × 3 | 4 | 3 | 12 |
| 6 × 4 | 6 | 4 | 24 |
| 3 × 7 | 3 | 7 | 21 |

**5**  3182 → 3282 → 2282 → 2182 → 3182
This happens for any number.

## Practice ■ 13b

**1**  **1.** 15  **2.** 5
**3.** Children's answers may vary.
**4.** 349  **5.** 50  **6.** 7
**7.** 150  **8.** 24  **9.** 190

**2**  Children's answers will vary. Make sure that the shapes they draw meet the requirements given.

**3**

| × | 2 | 3 | 4 |
|---|---|---|---|
| 9 | 18 | 27 | 36 |
| 6 | 12 | 18 | 24 |

| × | 2 | 5 | 10 |
|---|---|---|---|
| 5 | 10 | 25 | 50 |
| 8 | 16 | 40 | 80 |

| × | 4 | 8 | 7 |
|---|---|---|---|
| 3 | 12 | 24 | 21 |
| 5 | 20 | 40 | 35 |

| × | 3 | 2 | 7 |
|---|---|---|---|
| 10 | 30 | 20 | 70 |
| 3 | 9 | 6 | 21 |

## Practice ■ 12b

**1**  **1.** 16  **2.** 87  **3.** 385
**4.** 12  **5.** 49  **6.** 105
**7.** 100  **8.** 8  **9.** 50

**2**

**1.**   **2.**
mirror line   mirror line

**3.**   **4.**
mirror line   mirror line

**3**  **1.** 10 cm  **2.** 100 mm

**4**  Children's answers may vary.

## Practice ■ 13a

**1**  **1.** 12  **2.** 120  **3.** 83
**4.** 80  **5.** 85  **6.** 45
**7.** 2295  **8.** 526  **9.** 491

**2**

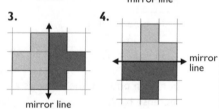

| × | 2 | 5 | 4 |
|---|---|---|---|
| 8 | 16 | 40 | 32 |
| 3 | 6 | 15 | 12 |

| × | 3 | 10 | 4 |
|---|---|---|---|
| 9 | 27 | 90 | 36 |
| 5 | 15 | 50 | 20 |

**4** 1. 120    2. 430    3. 1310

**5** Children's answers may vary.

## Practice ■ 14a

**1** 1. 46    2. 7040    3. 100
   4. 130    5. 24    6. 6
   7. 239    8. 4    9. 6996

**2** 1. 210, 30    2. 240, 6
   3. 5, 90

**3** Any of the following:

$\frac{1}{2}$ one half    $\frac{1}{3}$ one third

$\frac{1}{4}$ one quarter    $\frac{1}{10}$ one tenth

$\frac{2}{3}$ two thirds    $\frac{2}{4}$ two quarters

$\frac{2}{10}$ two tenths

$\frac{3}{4}$ three quarters    $\frac{3}{10}$ three tenths

$\frac{4}{10}$ four tenths

**4**

| $1 + 2 + 3 = 6$ | $4 + 5 + 6 = 15$ |
| $3 \times 2 = 6$ | $3 \times 5 = 15$ |

| $9 + 10 + 11 = 30$ |
| $3 \times 10 = 30$ |

Other answers will vary.

**5**

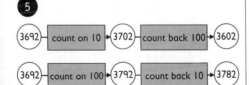

Other answers will vary.

## Practice ■ 14b

**1** 1. 9    2. 15    3. 130
   4. 6407    5. 8    6. 8
   7. 7888    8. 660    9. 5

**2**

| double | 20 | 100 | 28 | 40 | 64 | 92 | 360 | 740 | 5200 |
|---|---|---|---|---|---|---|---|---|---|
| number | 10 | 50 | 14 | 20 | 32 | 46 | 180 | 370 | 2600 |
| half | 5 | 25 | 7 | 10 | 16 | 23 | 90 | 185 | 1300 |

**3** 1. $\frac{1}{4}, \frac{3}{4}$    2. $\frac{2}{5}, \frac{3}{5}$

3. $\frac{3}{8}, \frac{5}{8}$    4. $\frac{3}{6} = \frac{1}{2}$

**4** 1. 12 days
   2. 12 days
   3. 3 large and 2 small or
      1 large and 5 small

**5** 1.    From:
         44–39         43–38
         42–37         41–36
         40–35

   2.    454–399      453–398
         ... 400–345

   3.    4554–3999   4553–3998
         ... 4000–3445

## Practice ■ 15a

**1** 1. 6    2. 1380    3. 18
   4. 6    5. 296    6. 150
   7. 18    8. 104    9. 250

**2**

| number | 12 | 24 | 36 | 60 | 120 | 600 |
|---|---|---|---|---|---|---|
| half | 6 | 12 | 18 | 30 | 60 | 300 |
| quarter | 3 | 6 | 9 | 15 | 30 | 150 |
| third | 4 | 8 | 12 | 20 | 40 | 200 |

**3**   **1.** 0      **2.** 4, 6 or 8
**3.** 0 or 5

**4**   **1.** March    **2.** 8:15
**3.** 3 p.m.    **4.** 1 day

**5**   Children's answers may vary.

## Practice ▪ 15b

**1**   **1.** 4      **2.** 190    **3.** 14
**4.** 28    **5.** 4444   **6.** 52
**7.** 43    **8.** 67    **9.** 32

**2**   8    22    40    86    300

**3**   divisible by 5       divisible by 2
divisible by 3       divisible by 10

**4**   **1.** £14.98   **2.** £24   **3.** £7.98

**5**   3 coins: 50p, 50p, 50p
4 coins: £1, 20p, 20p, 10p
5 coins: 50p, 50p, 20p, 20p, 10p
6 coins: £1, 10p, 10p, 10p, 10p, 10p
        £1, 20p, 10p, 10p, 5p, 5p
        50p, 50p, 20p, 10p, 10p, 10p

## Practice ▪ 16a

**1**   **1.** 500    **2.** 27    **3.** 143
**4.** 90    **5.** 58    **6.** 6
**7.** 20    **8.** 497   **9.** 835

**2**   **1.** 250m   **2.** 3 jugs   **3.** 900 g

**3**   **1.** 3      **2.** 12    **3.** 29

**4**   $\frac{1}{2} + \frac{1}{2}$      $\frac{1}{4} + \frac{3}{4}$

$\frac{3}{10} + \frac{7}{10}$      $\frac{3}{4} + \frac{1}{4}$

$\frac{5}{8} + \frac{3}{8}$      $\frac{1}{3} + \frac{2}{3}$

**5**   Children's answers may vary.

## Practice ▪ 16b

**1**   **1.** 48    **2.** 57    **3.** 287
**4.** 5     **5.** 31    **6.** 1
**7.** 8001   **8.** 2     **9.** 12

**2**   **1.** 9:10   **2.** 11:35   **3.** 2:20
**4.** 4:55   **5.** 7:05

**3**   **1.** 2000 m   **2.** $\frac{1}{2}$ litre
**3.** 2·5 kg      **4.** 1·5 m

**4**   **a** 5 (4 + 1 large)   **b** 3    **c** 3

**5**   Children's answers may vary.

## Practice ▪ 17a

**1**   **1.** 15    **2.** 118   **3.** 60
**4.** 160   **5.** 1997   **6.** 7950
**7.** 35    **8.** 3     **9.** 98

**2**

| × 10 | 700 | 200 | 5000 | 600 | 400 | 9000 | 800 |
|------|-----|-----|------|-----|-----|------|-----|
| number | 70 | 20 | 500 | 60 | 40 | 900 | 80 |
| ÷ 10 | 7 | 2 | 50 | 6 | 4 | 90 | 8 |

**3**   **1.** 8:45 p.m.    **2.** 12:30 a.m.
**3.** 1:15 a.m.    **4.** 6:30 p.m.

**4**   Helena: 90 stickers;
Lena: 100 stickers;
Rowan: 27 stickers.

**5** Any of the following:

$$500 + 600 = 1100$$
$$500 + 700 = 1200$$
$$500 + 800 = 1300$$
$$500 + 900 = 1400$$
$$600 + 700 = 1300$$
$$600 + 800 = 1400$$
$$600 + 900 = 1500$$
$$700 + 800 = 1500$$
$$700 + 900 = 1600$$
$$800 + 900 = 1700$$

## Practice ▪ 17b

**1**
| | | |
|---|---|---|
| 1. 9 | 2. 17 | 3. 156 |
| 4. 21 | 5. 5000 | 6. 939 |
| 7. 2 | 8. 280 | 9. 75 |

**2** 1. orange 2. 2    3. red

**3** a: 10   b: 30   c: 50
   d: 70   e: 90

**4** Children's answers may vary.

## Practice ▪ 18a

**1**
| | | |
|---|---|---|
| 1. 25 | 2. 18 | 3. 24 |
| 4. 470 | 5. 7 | 6. 36 |
| 7. 4333 | 8. 600 | 9. 2425 |

**2** Any of the following:

| | | | |
|---|---|---|---|
| 2 + 1 | 2 + 7 | 2 + 13 | 4 + 5 |
| 4 + 11 | 10 + 5 | 10 + 11 | 6 + 3 |
| 6 + 9 | 8 + 1 | 8 + 7 | |
| 8 + 13 | 12 + 3 | 2 + 13 | |
| 12 + 9 | 14 + 1 | 14 + 13 | |
| 14 + 7 | | | |

**3** Any numbers from 275 to 284.
Any numbers from 105 to 114.
Any numbers from 495 to 504.

Any numbers from 445 to 454.

**4** 1. wrong    2. correct
   3. wrong    4. wrong

**5** Any of the following:

| | |
|---|---|
| $700 - 7 = 693$ | $70 - 7 = 63$ |
| $400 - 4 = 396$ | $40 - 4 = 36$ |
| $600 - 6 = 594$ | $60 - 6 = 54$ |
| $300 - 3 = 297$ | $30 - 3 = 27$ |
| $900 - 9 = 891$ | $90 - 9 = 81$ |
| $500 - 5 = 495$ | $50 - 5 = 45$ |

## Practice ▪ 18b

**1**
| | | |
|---|---|---|
| 1. 10 | 2. 2000 | 3. 8 |
| 4. 5 | 5. 74 | 6. 496 |
| 7. 36 | 8. 20 | 9. 2 |

**2** Any of the following:

| | |
|---|---|
| $130 + 20 = 150$ | $130 - 20 = 110$ |
| $130 + 70 = 200$ | $130 - 70 = 60$ |
| $130 + 90 = 220$ | $130 - 90 = 40$ |
| $130 + 60 = 190$ | $130 - 60 = 70$ |
| $160 + 20 = 180$ | $160 - 20 = 140$ |
| $160 + 70 = 230$ | $160 - 70 = 90$ |
| $160 + 90 = 250$ | $160 - 90 = 70$ |
| $160 + 60 = 220$ | $160 - 60 = 100$ |
| $110 + 20 = 130$ | $110 - 20 = 90$ |
| $110 + 70 = 180$ | $110 - 70 = 40$ |
| $110 + 90 = 200$ | $110 - 90 = 20$ |
| $110 + 60 = 170$ | $110 - 60 = 50$ |
| $100 + 20 = 120$ | $100 - 20 = 80$ |
| $100 + 70 = 170$ | $100 - 70 = 30$ |
| $100 + 90 = 190$ | $100 - 90 = 10$ |
| $100 + 60 = 160$ | $100 - 60 = 40$ |

**3**
| | |
|---|---|
| $29 \rightarrow 2900$ | $137 \rightarrow 13\,700$ |
| $4 \rightarrow 400$ | $60 \rightarrow 6000$ |
| $528 \rightarrow 52\,800$ | $100 \rightarrow 10\,000$ |
| $10 \rightarrow 1000$ | $701 \rightarrow 70\,100$ |

**4**   **1.** 36 candles   **2.** 36 candles; £2.97
     **3.** 4          **4.** 46p

**5**   Children's answers may vary.

## Practice ▪ 19a

**1**   **1.** 8       **2.** 50     **3.** 200
     **4.** 21     **5.** 170   **6.** 60
     **7.** 702   **8.** 3070   **9.** 900

**2**   **1.** 113   **2.** 114   **3.** 162
     **4.** 85    **5.** 114   **6.** 135

**3**   **1.** 326 miles    **2.** 400 children
     **3.** 82 passengers

**4**   Any of the following:

     300, 700       250, 750
     850, 150       350, 650
     800, 200       900, 100
     450, 550       600, 400

**5**   Children's answers may vary.

## Practice ▪ 19b

**1**   **1.** 45     **2.** 14    **3.** 80
     **4.** 3000   **5.** 70    **6.** 840
     **7.** 140    **8.** 78    **9.** 20

**2**   50, 50    37, 63    42, 58    26, 74
     90, 10    65, 35    81, 19    1, 99

**3**   **1.** 25    **2.** 25    **3.** 28
     **4.** 27    **5.** 59    **6.** 9

**4**   Children's answers may vary.

     $5 + 8 + 27 = 40$
     $5 + 8 + 42 = 55$
     $5 + 8 + 55 = 68$
     $5 + 19 + 27 = 51$
     $5 + 19 + 42 = 66$

$5 + 19 + 55 = 79$
$5 + 36 + 27 = 68$
$5 + 36 + 42 = 83$
$5 + 36 + 55 = 96$

$8 + 8 + 27 = 43$
$8 + 8 + 42 = 58$
$8 + 8 + 55 = 71$
$8 + 19 + 27 = 54$
$8 + 19 + 42 = 69$
$8 + 19 + 55 = 82$
$8 + 36 + 27 = 71$
$8 + 36 + 42 = 86$
$8 + 36 + 55 = 99$

$14 + 8 + 27 = 49$
$14 + 8 + 42 = 64$
$14 + 8 + 55 = 77$
$14 + 19 + 27 = 60$
$14 + 19 + 42 = 75$
$14 + 19 + 55 = 88$
$14 + 36 + 27 = 77$
$14 + 36 + 42 = 92$
$14 + 36 + 55 = 105$

**5**   155, 8, 147      8, 417, 409
     6, 371, 365      371, 9, 362
     803, 7, 796      7, 234, 227
     155, 6, 149      6, 803, 797
     8, 371, 363      371, 7, 364
     417, 9, 408      9, 234, 225

## Practice ▪ 20a

**1**   **1.** 29    **2.** 1000   **3.** 133
     **4.** 800   **5.** 6      **6.** 6
     **7.** 427   **8.** 8      **9.** 73

**2**   240

**3**   **1.** 45 minutes    **2.** 50 minutes
     **3.** 31 days

**4**   **1.** £65    **2.** £905   **3.** £25

**5** $3 \times 7 = 21$   $6 \times 10 = 60$
$5 \times 9 = 45$   $2 \times 9 = 18$ **or** $3 \times 6 = 18$
$4 \times 8 = 32$   $4 \times 7 = 28$

## Practice ▪ 20b

**1**  1. 185   2. 200   3. 10
4. 9   5. 92   6. 10
7. 10   8. 47   9. 50

**2**  $36 \to 720$     $17 \to 340$
$42 \to 840$     $59 \to 1180$
$130 \to 2600$     $250 \to 5000$

**3**  $27 + 81 = 27 \times 4$
double $29 = 580 \div 10$
$311 - 289 =$ one half of 44
$16 \times 5 = 8000 \div 100$
$146 + 24 = 17 \times 10$
one half of $32 = 512 - 496$

**4**  $\frac{1}{2}$ kg $= 500$ g     $\frac{1}{4}$ l $= 250$ ml

$\frac{3}{4}$ l $= 750$ ml     $\frac{1}{5}$ kg $= 200$ g

$\frac{1}{4}$ kg $= 250$ g     $\frac{1}{10}$ l $= 100$ ml

**5**  Any of the following:

$1000 - 200 = 800$
$1100 - 300 = 800$
$1200 - 400 = 800$
$1300 - 500 = 800$
$1400 - 600 = 800$
$1500 - 700 = 800$
$1600 - 800 = 800$
$1700 - 900 = 800$

## Practice ▪ 21a

**1**  1. 40   2. 13   3. 794
4. 14   5. 5   6. 1500
7. 140   8. 27   9. 20

**2**  1.
$\overbrace{\phantom{xxxx}}^{+20}\ \overbrace{\phantom{xx}}^{+3}$
36            56  59

2.
$\overbrace{\phantom{xxxx}}^{+60}\ \overbrace{\phantom{xx}}^{+4}$
28            88  92

3.
$\overbrace{\phantom{xxxx}}^{+10}\ \overbrace{\phantom{xx}}^{+7}$
42        52        59

4.
$\overbrace{\phantom{xxxx}}^{+70}\ \overbrace{\phantom{xx}}^{+5}$
18            88  93

5.
$\overbrace{\phantom{xxxx}}^{+30}\ \overbrace{\phantom{xx}}^{+2}$
59            89  91

6.
$\overbrace{\phantom{xxxx}}^{+40}\ \overbrace{\phantom{xx}}^{+9}$
53            93  102

**3**  1. g   2. ml   3. kg
4. kg   5. l   6. ml

**4**  triangle → tetrahedron
square → cube
circle → cone, cylinder, hemisphere

**5**  Any ten from:

$305 \to 30\,500$
$309 \to 30\,900$
$350 \to 35\,000$
$390 \to 39\,000$
$503 \to 50\,300$
$509 \to 50\,900$
$903 \to 90\,300$
$905 \to 90\,500$
$930 \to 93\,000$
$950 \to 95\,000$
$359 \to 35\,900$
$395 \to 39\,500$
$539 \to 53\,900$
$593 \to 59\,300$
$935 \to 93\,500$
$953 \to 95\,300$

## Practice ▪ 21b

**1**  1. 17   2. 7   3. 620
4. 100   5. 800   6. 1700
7. 2   8. 15   9. 2

**2**  Children's answers may vary

| | Number of quadrilateral faces | Number of triangular faces | Total number of faces |
|---|---|---|---|
| square prism | 6 | 0 | 6 |
| triangular-based pyramid | 0 | 4 | 4 |
| triangular prism | 3 | 2 | 5 |
| square-based pyramid | 1 | 4 | 5 |

**4**

| 3 | 7 | 9 | 2 |
|---|---|---|---|
| 6 | 4 | 4 | 5 |

Children's answers may vary for the remaining grids.

## Practice ■ 22a

**1**  1. 1200  2. 24  3. 140
4. 50p  5. 6  6. 170
7. 24  8. 53  9. 67

**2**  1. 2 kg  2. 3·5 kg  3. 400 g
4. 1·7 kg  5. 4·1 kg

**3**  1. pyramid  2. cuboid
3. cube  4. cylinder

**4**  1. 800 teabags
2. £19.90
3. 2·5 kg or $2\frac{1}{2}$ kg

**5**  Children's answers may vary.

## Practice ■ 22b

**1**  1. 70  2. 1  3. 40
4. 9  5. 6  6. 36
7. 4050  8. 7000  9. 1 m

**2**  $\frac{1}{4}$ l = 250 ml    $\frac{1}{10}$ l = 100 ml
$\frac{3}{4}$ l = 750 ml    3 l = 3000 ml
2 l = 2000 ml

**3**  1. £8  2. £30
3. £44  4. £30

**4**  1. × ×  2. + +  3. + −
4. + −  5. × ÷  6. − −

**5**  67 + 89 = 156    76 + 89 = 165
78 + 69 = 147    87 + 69 = 156
68 + 79 = 147    86 + 79 = 165

Two additions give the same answer when the units remain the same and the tens are interchanged, e.g. 67 + 89 = 87 + 69.

## Practice ■ 23a

**1**  1. 5  2. 280  3. 13
4. 100  5. 15  6. 1000
7. 70  8. 91  9. 8

**2**  $\frac{1}{2}$ kg, 500 g    $\frac{1}{10}$ kg, 100 g
$\frac{3}{4}$ kg, 750 g    $\frac{1}{4}$ kg, 250 g
$\frac{1}{4}$ l, 250 ml    $\frac{1}{2}$ l, 500 ml
$\frac{1}{10}$ l, 100 ml

**3**  Children's answers may vary.

**4**  triangular prism
pentagonal prism
pentagonal-based pyramid
square-based pyramid

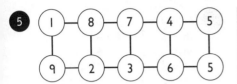

**5**

## Practice ▪ 23b

**1**   **1.** 10    **2.** 19    **3.** 47
    **4.** 140   **5.** 29    **6.** 17
    **7.** 200 g   **8.** 591   **9.** 196

**2**   Children's answers may vary.
    For example:

$$16 - 4 - 10 = 2$$
$$22 + 6 - 16 = 12$$
$$13 \times 2 \times 5 = 130$$
$$28 + 16 + 12 = 56$$
$$24 \div 3 \times 4 = 32$$
$$5 \times 8 \div 4 = 10$$

**3**   **1.** $2\frac{1}{2}$ litres or 2 litres 500 ml
    **2.** 200 cm or 2 m
    **3.** 1228 g

**4**   a: −18      b: −17
    c: −14      d: −12
    e: −9       f: −7
    g: −3      h: −2

**5**   The patterns are given until the fifth
    row below.

| | |
|---|---|
| 30 + 10 = 40 | 30 − 10 = 20 |
| 40 + 10 = 50 | 40 − 10 = 30 |
| 50 + 10 = 60 | 50 − 10 = 40 |
| 60 + 10 = 70 | 60 − 10 = 50 |
| 70 + 10 = 80 | 70 − 10 = 60 |

| | |
|---|---|
| 30 × 10 = 300 | 30 ÷ 10 = 3 |
| 40 × 10 = 400 | 40 ÷ 10 = 4 |
| 50 × 10 = 500 | 50 ÷ 10 = 5 |
| 60 × 10 = 600 | 60 ÷ 10 = 6 |
| 70 × 10 = 700 | 70 ÷ 10 = 7 |

## Practice ▪ 24a

**1**   **1.** 207    **2.** 69    **3.** 17
    **4.** 25p   **5.** 50    **6.** 280
    **7.** 80    **8.** 29    **9.** 36

**2**   **1.** 39 + 57    **2.** 73 − 28
    **3.** 15 + 66    **4.** 84 − 79
    **5. & 6.** Children's answers may
    vary.

**3**   Children's answers may vary.

**4**   **1.** 18 minutes
    **2.** Wednesday 9th April
    **3.** 10:45

**5**   Children's answers may vary.

## Practice ▪ 24b

**1**   **1.** 18     **2.** 700   **3.** 71
    **4.** 9      **5.** 6     **6.** 9
    **7.** 2000   **8.** £5    **9.** 80

**2**   **1.** number of hours × 60
    **2.** number of tickets × 4

**3**

| × 6 | × 7 | × 8 | × 9 |
|---|---|---|---|
| 24 | 21 | 72 | 0 |
| 48 | 49 | 48 | 90 |
| 30 | 14 | 32 | 63 |

**4**   **1.** 4 min 40 sec    **2.** 2 hr 40 min
    **3.** 2:30 p.m.

**5**

720 ÷ 10 = 72   750 ÷ 10 = 75   780 ÷ 10 = 78
270 ÷ 10 = 27   250 ÷ 10 = 25   280 ÷ 10 = 28
570 ÷ 10 = 57   520 ÷ 10 = 52   580 ÷ 10 = 58
870 ÷ 10 = 87   820 ÷ 10 = 82   850 ÷ 10 = 85

## Practice ▪ 25a

**1**
1. 19    2. 290    3. 1000
4. 200    5. 10p    6. 2150
7. 7    8. 11    9. 19

**2**
1. 17, 51, 102 → 102
2. 16, 64, 128 → 128
3. 44, 88, 176 → 176

**3**   148   185   222   259   296

**4**

| + 19 | 56 | 94 | 176 | 305 | 448 | 582 | 421 |
|------|----|----|-----|-----|-----|-----|-----|
| number | 37 | 75 | 157 | 286 | 429 | 563 | 402 |
| – 19 | 18 | 56 | 138 | 267 | 410 | 544 | 383 |

**5**   Children's answers may vary.

## Practice ▪ 25b

**1**
1. 520    2. 5000    3. 2
4. 6    5. 75    6. £2.50
7. 5    8. 29    9. 4333

**2**
8 → 160      14 → 280
32 → 640      120 → 2400
471 → 9420      208 → 4160

**3**
$5 \times 17 = (5 \times 10) + (5 \times 7)$
$= 50 + 35 = 85$
Children's answers may vary.

**4**
$2 \times 3 = 3 + 3$
$6 \times 7 = 7 + 7 + 7 + 7 + 7 + 7$
$11 \times 5 = 11 + 11 + 11 + 11 + 11$
$29 \times 4 = 29 + 29 + 29 + 29$
$52 \times 8 = 52 + 52 + 52 + 52 + 52 +$
$52 + 52 + 52$

**5**
$72 = 8 \times 9$
$16 = 2 \times 8$ or $4 \times 4$
$24 = 3 \times 8$ or $4 \times 6$
$42 = 6 \times 7$      $81 = 9 \times 9$
$54 = 6 \times 9$      $63 = 7 \times 9$
$48 = 6 \times 8$

## Practice ▪ 26a

**1**
1. 16    2. 4040    3. 20p
4. 94    5. 21    6. 416
7. 600    8. 26    9. 61

**2**
a: $\frac{1}{8}$    b: $\frac{2}{8}, \frac{1}{4}$    c: $\frac{4}{8}, \frac{1}{2}$
d: $\frac{5}{8}$    e: $\frac{7}{8}$    f: $\frac{15}{16}$

**3**
1. 4    2. 6    3. 5
4. 4    5. 4    6. 5

**4**
1. 407    2. 387    3. 572
4. 234    5. 704    6. 675

**5**   Children's answers may vary.

## Practice ▪ 26b

**1**
1. 25    2. 200    3. 170
4. 130    5. 7    6. 55
7. 31    8. 32    9. 22

**2**

| | ×2 | ×3 | ×4 | ×5 | ×6 |
|----|----|----|-----|-----|-----|
| 23 | 46 | 69 | 92 | 115 | 138 |
| 42 | 84 | 126 | 168 | 210 | 252 |
| 34 | 68 | 102 | 136 | 170 | 204 |
| 13 | 26 | 39 | 52 | 65 | 78 |
| 26 | 52 | 78 | 104 | 130 | 156 |
| 44 | 88 | 132 | 176 | 220 | 264 |

**3**　**1.** $6 \times 7$　**2.** $8 \times 9$　**3.** $4 \times 8$
　　**4.** $9 \times 6$　**5.** $9 \times 3$　**6.** $8 \times 7$

**4**　Any of the following:

| | |
|---|---|
| $144 \div 2 = 72$ | $208 \div 8 = 26$ |
| $235 \div 5 = 47$ | $378 \div 6 = 63$ |
| $378 \div 7 = 54$ | $378 \div 9 = 42$ |
| $180 \div 5 = 36$ | $180 \div 6 = 30$ |
| $180 \div 9 = 20$ | $333 \div 9 = 37$ |
| $182 \div 7 = 26$ | $207 \div 9 = 23$ |
| $208 \div 2 = 104$ | $189 \div 9 = 21$ |
| $160 \div 2 = 80$ | $144 \div 6 = 24$ |
| $160 \div 8 = 20$ | $144 \div 8 = 18$ |
| $180 \div 2 = 90$ | $180 \div 3 = 60$ |
| $333 \div 3 = 111$ | $189 \div 3 = 63$ |
| $207 \div 3 = 69$ | |

**5**　Children's answers may vary.

## Practice ▪ 27a

**1**　**1.** 5　　**2.** 6　　**3.** 32
　　**4.** 6　　**5.** 10　**6.** 38
　　**7.** 160　**8.** 100　**9.** 12

**2**　**1.** 300 g　　　　**2.** 4·8 kg

　　**3.** $\frac{100}{400}$ or $\frac{1}{4}$

**3**
| | | |
|---|---|---|
| 5, 15, 5 | 5, 20, 5 | 5, 25, 5 |
| 6, 18, 6 | 6, 24, 6 | 6, 30, 6 |
| 7, 21, 7 | 7, 28, 7 | 7, 35, 7 |
| 8, 24, 8 | 8, 32, 8 | 8, 40, 8 |
| 9, 27, 9 | 9, 36, 9 | 9, 45, 9 |
| 10, 30, 10 | 10, 40, 10 | 10, 50, 10 |

**4**　**1.** 5 tables　**2.** 7 crayons
　　**3.** 8 books

**5**

| amount | ÷ 2 | ÷ 4 | ÷ 5 | ÷ 10 |
|---|---|---|---|---|
| £40 | £20 | £10 | £8 | £4 |
| £6 | £3 | £1.50 | £1.20 | £0.60 |
| £10.60 | £5.30 | £2.65 | £2.12 | £1.06 |
| £22.40 | £11.20 | £5.60 | £4.48 | £2.24 |
| £37.20 | £18.60 | £9.30 | £7.44 | £3.72 |
| £100 | £50 | £25 | £20 | £10 |
| £92.80 | £46.40 | £23.20 | £18.56 | £9.28 |

## Practice ▪ 27b

**1**　**1.** 0　　　　　　**2.** 10　　**3.** 400
　　**4.** 160　　　　　**5.** 27　　**6.** 11
　　**7.** any number　**8.** 43　　**9.** 46

**2**

| | |
|---|---|
| $10 \times 3 = 30$ | $10 \times 6 = 60$ |
| $11 \times 3 = 33$ | $20 \times 6 = 120$ |
| $12 \times 3 = 36$ | $30 \times 6 = 180$ |
| $13 \times 3 = 39$ | $40 \times 6 = 240$ |
| $14 \times 3 = 42$ | $50 \times 6 = 300$ |
| $15 \times 3 = 45$ | $60 \times 6 = 360$ |
| $16 \times 3 = 48$ | $70 \times 6 = 420$ |

| | |
|---|---|
| $11 \times 9 = 99$ | $8 \div 8 = 1$ |
| $22 \times 9 = 198$ | $80 \div 8 = 10$ |
| $33 \times 9 = 297$ | $800 \div 8 = 100$ |
| $44 \times 9 = 396$ | $8000 \div 8 = 1000$ |
| $55 \times 9 = 495$ | $80\,000 \div 8 = 10\,000$ |
| $66 \times 9 = 594$ | $800\,000 \div 8 = 100\,000$ |
| $77 \times 9 = 693$ | $8\,000\,000 \div 8 = 1\,000\,000$ |

**3**

| less than $\frac{1}{2}$ | equal to $\frac{1}{2}$ | more than $\frac{1}{2}$ |
|---|---|---|
| $\frac{1}{3}$　$\frac{1}{8}$　$\frac{1}{4}$ | $\frac{3}{6}$　$\frac{2}{4}$　$\frac{4}{8}$ | $\frac{5}{8}$　$\frac{2}{3}$ |

**4** tennis set and football: £16.48
tennis set and cricket bat: £22.98
tennis set and hockey stick: £18.18
football and cricket bat: £19.48
football and hockey stick: £14.68
cricket bat and hockey stick: £21.18

**5**

$10 - 1 = 11 - 2 = 12 - 3 = 13 - 4 = 14 - 5$
$= 15 - 6 = 16 - 7 = 17 - 8 = 18 - 9 = 9$

$10 - 2 = 11 - 3 = 12 - 4 = 13 - 5 = 14 - 6$
$= 15 - 7 = 16 - 8 = 17 - 9 = 8$

$10 - 3 = 11 - 4 = 12 - 5 = 13 - 6 = 14 - 7$
$= 15 - 8 = 16 - 9 = 7$

$10 - 4 = 11 - 5 = 12 - 6 = 13 - 7 = 14 - 8$
$= 15 - 9 = 6$

## Practice ▪ 28a

**1**   **1.** 88    **2.** 21    **3.** 4900
   **4.** 39    **5.** 48    **6.** 2
   **7.** 550    **8.** 50 cm   **9.** 3

**2**   **1.** 0·7    **2.** 1·5    **3.** 52·3
   **4.** 100·1   **5.** 202·2   **6.** 40·6

**3**   **1.** 286 children
   **2.** 159 passengers
   **3.** 468 books

**4**   ascending by 1
   ascending by 99
   numbers unchanged
   answers all zero

**5**   Children's answers may vary.

## Practice ▪ 28b

**1**   **1.** 13    **2.** 42    **3.** 3
   **4.** 9    **5.** 2    **6.** 600
   **7.** 8    **8.** 27    **9.** 19

**2**   $0·5, \frac{1}{2}$    $0·3, \frac{3}{10}$    $0·75, \frac{3}{4}$

   $0·1, \frac{1}{10}$    $0·8, \frac{4}{5}$    $0·25, \frac{1}{4}$

   $0·4, \frac{2}{5}$

**3**   Children's answers may vary.

**4**   **1.** Monday    **2.** 7th June
   **3.** 17 minutes to 12 (11:43 a.m.)
   **4.** 30 days    **5.** 1000 years

**5**   Children's answers may vary.

## Practice ▪ 29a

**1**   **1.** 57    **2.** 27    **3.** 1000
   **4.** 14    **5.** 4    **6.** 2
   **7.** 39    **8.** 810    **9.** 137

**2**   **1.**    or

   **2.**

   **3.** any quadrilateral
   **4.** any pentagon

**3**   **1.** 20p, 20p, 10p
   **2.** £1, £1, £1, 5p
   **3.** £2, £2, 10p, 5p, 2p
   **4.** £1, £1, 50p, 20p, 2p, 1p
     **or** £2, 50p, 10p, 10p, 2p, 1p

**4** Any of the following:
  **1.** 5·1, 5·2, 5·3, 5·4, 5·5, 5·6, 5·7, 5.8
  **2.** 4·2, 4·3, 4·4
  **3.** 3·1, 3·2

**5** Children's answers may vary.

## Practice ▪ 29b

**1** **1.** 700  **2.** 2  **3.** 4
  **4.** 15  **5.** 72  **6.** 35
  **7.** 8000  **8.** 3  **9.** 2996

**2** **1.** south  **2.** north-east
  **3.** west  **4.** south-west
  **5.** east

**3** 0·9  1·4  2·3  3·2  4·1
  8p  £0.70  80p  88p  £1.08
  0·45 kg  0·5 kg  1·03 kg  3·1 kg  5·4 kg
  0·08 m  0·78 m  0·87 m  7·8 m  8·7 m

**4** 4165 + 7 = 4172   7 + 3038 = 3045
  8 + 9297 = 9305   9297 + 6 = 9303
  1283 + 9 = 1292   9 + 6999 = 7008
  4165 + 8 = 4173   8 + 1283 = 1291
  7 + 9297 = 9304   9297 + 9 = 9306
  3038 + 6 = 3044   6 + 6999 = 7005

**5**

| | 5 | 3 | | or | | 4 | 8 | |
|---|---|---|---|---|---|---|---|---|
| 12 | 9 | 7 | 2 | | 10 | 12 | 2 | 6 |
| 11 | 8 | 10 | 1 | | 7 | 9 | 11 | 3 |
| | 4 | 6 | | | | 1 | 5 | |

## Practice ▪ 30a

**1** **1.** 33  **2.** 21  **3.** 32
  **4.** 7  **5.** 25 cm  **6.** 2
  **7.** 2900  **8.** 36  **9.** 150

**2** **1.** 5 minutes  **2.** 6 hours
  **3.** 10 minutes

**3** **1.** 37, 39, 41
  **2.** 145, 147, 149
  **3.** 371, 373, 375
  **4.** 999, 1001, 1003
  **5.** 8299, 8301, 8303
  **6.** 9997, 9999, 10001

**4** (1,2)  (3,4)  (5,2)  (3,0)
  intersection of diagonals at (3,2)

**5** 3·4, 3·5, 4·3, 4·5, 5·3, 5·4

## Practice ▪ 30b

**1** **1.** 40  **2.** 6  **3.** 6
  **4.** 45  **5.** 10  **6.** 56
  **7.** 28  **8.** 2200  **9.** 60

**2** a: (3,8)  b: (5,8)  c: (5,7)
  d: (8,4)  e: (7,4)  f: (6,5)
  g: (6,1)  h: (5,1)  i: (5,3)
  j: (3,3)  k: (3,1)  l: (2,1)
  m: (2,5)  n: (1,4)  p: (0,4)
  q: (3,7)

**3** Children's answers may vary.

**4** **1.** 96 biscuits  **2.** 7 biscuits
  **3.** 6 biscuits

**5** Any of the following:

  39  93  35  53  37  73
  95  59  97  79  57  75

  Children's answers may vary – all
  numbers are odd, so the differences
  are even.

## Practice ▪ 31a

**1** **1.** 54  **2.** 1000  **3.** 17
  **4.** 12  **5.** 90  **6.** 2904
  **7.** 9  **8.** 200  **9.** 60

**2** 

$-10 \quad -8 \quad -6 \; -5 \quad -3 \quad -1 \quad 0$

**3**
1. 45, 101          2. 24, 106
3. 33, 151          4. 52, 80
5. 47, 125          6. 29, 125

**4**
1. Any of the following:

$14 + 11 + 11 \qquad 14 + 7 + 15$
$14 + 13 + 9 \qquad 14 + 8 + 14$
$14 + 12 + 10 \qquad 13 + 12 + 11$
$13 + 8 + 15 \qquad 15 + 9 + 12$
$15 + 10 + 11$

2. Any of the following:

$15 + 11 + 6 + 5$
$15 + 10 + 7 + 5$
$15 + 9 + 8 + 5$
$15 + 9 + 7 + 6$
$14 + 6 + 9 + 8$
$14 + 6 + 12 + 5$
$14 + 6 + 10 + 7$
$14 + 7 + 11 + 5$
$14 + 8 + 10 + 5$
$13 + 7 + 9 + 8$
$13 + 6 + 10 + 8$
$13 + 7 + 12 + 5$
$13 + 6 + 11 + 7$
$13 + 8 + 11 + 5$
$13 + 9 + 10 + 5$
$12 + 7 + 10 + 8$
$12 + 6 + 11 + 8$
$12 + 6 + 10 + 9$
$12 + 9 + 11 + 5$
$11 + 7 + 10 + 9$
$11 + 11 + 10 + 5$
$11 + 11 + 9 + 6$
$11 + 11 + 8 + 7$

3. Any of the following:

$6 + 5 + 7 + 8 + 12$
$6 + 5 + 7 + 9 + 11$
$6 + 5 + 8 + 10 + 9$

**5** Children's answers may vary.

## Practice ▪ 31b

**1**
1. 1120     2. 1        3. 54
4. 7        5. 10       6. 6
7. 50       8. 44       9. 40p

**2**
$315 - 89 = 226 \quad 252 - 89 = 163$
$315 - 37 = 278 \quad 252 - 37 = 215$
$315 - 96 = 219 \quad 252 - 96 = 156$
$403 - 89 = 314 \quad 514 - 89 = 425$
$403 - 37 = 366 \quad 514 - 37 = 477$
$403 - 96 = 307 \quad 514 - 96 = 418$
$691 - 89 = 602$
$691 - 37 = 654$
$691 - 96 = 595$

**3** Children's answers may vary. Here is one example:

4474    4473    3473    3472    2472

**4**

| nearest 10 | 370 | 300 | 950 | 110 | 650 | 700 | 830 | 280 |
|---|---|---|---|---|---|---|---|---|
| number | 369 | 298 | 951 | 107 | 649 | 703 | 825 | 276 |
| nearest 100 | 400 | 300 | 1000 | 100 | 600 | 700 | 800 | 300 |

**5** Children's answers may vary.

## Practice ▪ 32a

**1**
1. 100      2. 7        3. 2992
4. 53       5. 63       6. 13
7. 4        8. 70       9. 42

**2**
1. 76       2. 91       3. 102
4. 91       5. 73       6. 102

**3** 1. £8

2.

| Pair of items | Change |
|---|---|
| Soccer goal and pedal car | £7.02 |
| Skateboard and soccer goal | £76.02 |

3. £108.97

**4** 1. ÷    2. +    3. ×
4. ÷    5. −    6. ×

**5** The rectangles should have dimensions:

48 × 1, 24 × 2, 12 × 4, 8 × 6 or reversals

## Practice ▪ 32b

**1** 1. 49    2. 9    3. £1
4. 16    5. 4    6. 10
7. 2    8. 10    9. 16 000

**2** Children's answers may vary.

**3** Any of the following:

413 + 98 = 511    413 + 69 = 482
413 + 57 = 470
413 − 98 = 315    413 − 69 = 344
413 − 57 = 356
195 + 98 = 293    195 + 69 = 264
195 + 57 = 252
195 − 98 = 97    195 − 69 = 126
195 − 57 = 138
807 + 98 = 905    807 + 69 = 876
807 + 57 = 864
807 − 98 = 709    807 − 69 = 738
807 − 57 = 750

**4** a 50 mm   b 13 mm   c 52 mm
d 40 mm   e 22 mm   f 53 mm
g 15 mm

The perimeter of the first shape is 115 mm, and the perimeter of the second is 130 mm.

**5** Children's answers may vary.

## Practice ▪ 33a

**1** 1. 93    2. 3000    3. 8
4. 28    5. 10 cm    6. 16
7. 750    8. 5    9. 65

**2** 1. 2000 straws    2. 25 straws
3. 27 straws

**3** Any of the following:

$5 \times 8 = 40$     $5 \times 9 = 45$
$4 \times 8 = 32$     $4 \times 9 = 36$
$7 \times 8 = 56$     $7 \times 9 = 63$
$8 \times 8 = 64$     $8 \times 9 = 72$
$6 \times 8 = 48$     $6 \times 9 = 54$
$9 \times 8 = 72$     $9 \times 9 = 81$

**4** 1. 4 right angles    2. 90°
3. $\frac{1}{4}$ turn    4. $\frac{3}{4}$ turn
5. 180°

**5** Children's answers may vary.

## Practice ▪ 33b

**1** 1. 400    2. 250 cm    3. 7
4. 8000    5. 29    6. 240
7. 36    8. 9    9. 5200

**2** 1. 19    2. 23    3. 37
4. 37    5. 26    6. 18

**3** 1. 1 right angle clockwise
2. 1 right angle anti-clockwise
3. 1½ right angles clockwise

**4** 1. 2000 biscuits    2. 5 g
3. 20 days

**5** Children's answers may vary. The largest possible answer is 695.

## Practice ▪ 34a

**1** 1. 5    2. 18    3. 7154
4. 600    5. 50    6. 330
7. 42    8. 6    9. 1200

**2** 1. £6.07 (£6.00)
2. £13.81 (£13.80)
3. £14.60 (£14.60)
4. £17.98 (£18.00)

**3** Children's answers may vary.

**4** 1. 90°    1 right angle
2. 180°    2 right angles
3. 270°    3 right angles

**5**

Children's answers may vary.

## Practice ▪ 34b

**1** 1. 5    2. 85    3. 64
4. 72    5. 4    6. 4
7. 6    8. 314    9. 125 g

**2** 1. 90° anti-clockwise
2. 45° anti-clockwise
3. 135° anti-clockwise
4. 270° clockwise
5. 225° anti-clockwise

**3** 1. 5    2. Thursday
3. Monday

**4** The rectangles should have dimensions and area:

$15 \times 1$ ($15\,cm^2$), $14 \times 2$ ($28\,cm^2$),
$13 \times 3$ ($39\,cm^2$), $12 \times 4$ ($48\,cm^2$),
$11 \times 5$ ($55\,cm^2$), $10 \times 6$ ($60\,cm^2$),
$9 \times 7$ ($63\,cm^2$), $8 \times 8$ ($64\,cm^2$).

**5** $876 + 53 = 929$    $853 + 76 = 929$

## Practice ▪ 35a

**1** 1. 130    2. 48    3. 8
4. 108    5. 20 cm    6. 67
7. 38    8. 117    9. 269

**2** Children's answers may vary.

**3** 310

**4** $15 \times 7 = 105$      $7 \times 15 = 105$
$105 \div 7 = 15$      $105 \div 15 = 7$

$12 \times 9 = 108$      $9 \times 12 = 108$
$108 \div 9 = 12$      $108 \div 12 = 9$

$8 \times 14 = 112$      $14 \times 8 = 112$
$112 \div 14 = 8$      $112 \div 8 = 14$

$6 \times 16 = 96$      $16 \times 6 = 96$
$96 \div 16 = 6$      $96 \div 6 = 16$

$70 \times 20 = 1400$      $20 \times 70 = 1400$
$1400 \div 70 = 20$      $1400 \div 20 = 70$

**5** Children's answers may vary.

## Practice ▪ 35b

**1** 1. 23    2. 42    3. 550
4. 97    5. 30 000    6. 320
7. 50    8. 3    9. 60

**2**

| 20 | 70 | 50 |
|----|----|----|
| 80 |    | 130 |
| 60 | 140 | 80 |

| 32 | 86 | 54 |
|----|----|----|
| 98 |    | 83 |
| 66 | 95 | 29 |

Further answers may vary.

**3** The answer that they get will always be the same as the start number.

**4** Check that shapes are accurately drawn.

## Practice ▪ 36a

**1**  1. 901    2. 63    3. 5
   4. 28    5. 679    6. 7605
   7. 150    8. 311    9. 558

**2**

$13 \div 6 = 2$ rem 1    $13 \div 7 = 1$ rem 6
$13 \div 8 = 1$ rem 5    $13 \div 9 = 1$ rem 4

$17 \div 6 = 2$ rem 5    $17 \div 7 = 2$ rem 3
$17 \div 8 = 2$ rem 1    $17 \div 9 = 1$ rem 8

$22 \div 6 = 3$ rem 4    $22 \div 7 = 3$ rem 1
$22 \div 8 = 2$ rem 6    $22 \div 9 = 2$ rem 4

$29 \div 6 = 4$ rem 5    $29 \div 7 = 4$ rem 1
$29 \div 8 = 3$ rem 5    $29 \div 9 = 3$ rem 2

$31 \div 6 = 5$ rem 1    $31 \div 7 = 4$ rem 3
$31 \div 8 = 3$ rem 7    $31 \div 9 = 3$ rem 4

$58 \div 6 = 9$ rem 4    $58 \div 7 = 8$ rem 2
$58 \div 8 = 7$ rem 2    $58 \div 9 = 6$ rem 4

$75 \div 6 = 12$ rem 3    $75 \div 7 = 10$ rem 5
$75 \div 8 = 9$ rem 3    $75 \div 9 = 8$ rem 3

**3**

| double | 100 | 800 | 280 | 640 | 2000 | 1360 | 1000 |
|--------|-----|-----|-----|-----|------|------|------|
| number | 50 | 400 | 140 | 320 | 1000 | 680 | 500 |
| half | 25 | 200 | 70 | 160 | 500 | 340 | 250 |

**4**  1. 8 boxes    2. 7 cakes
   3. 12 lengths

**5** Children's answers may vary.

## Practice ▪ 36b

**1**  1. 300    2. 30    3. 300
   4. 428    5. 171    6. 10
   7. 60    8. 6000    9. 81

**2**  21    27    47    66    98    251

**3** Children's answers may vary.

**4**

| number | 8 | 24 | 56 | 120 | 224 | 320 | 488 |
|--------|---|----|----|-----|-----|-----|-----|
| halve | 4 | 12 | 28 | 60 | 112 | 160 | 244 |
| halve again | 2 | 6 | 14 | 30 | 56 | 80 | 122 |
| halve again | 1 | 3 | 7 | 15 | 28 | 40 | 61 |

**5**

| number | 1 | 2 | 3 | 4 | 5 | 6 | 7 | 8 | 9 |
|--------|---|---|---|---|---|---|---|---|---|
| x 2 | 2 | 4 | 6 | 8 | 10 | 12 | 14 | 16 | 18 |
| x 3 | 3 | 6 | 9 | 12 | 15 | 18 | 21 | 24 | 27 |
| x 4 | 4 | 8 | 12 | 16 | 20 | 24 | 28 | 32 | 36 |
| x 5 | 5 | 10 | 15 | 20 | 25 | 30 | 35 | 40 | 45 |
| x 6 | 6 | 12 | 18 | 24 | 30 | 36 | 42 | 48 | 54 |
| x 7 | 7 | 14 | 21 | 28 | 35 | 42 | 49 | 56 | 63 |
| x 8 | 8 | 16 | 24 | 32 | 40 | 48 | 56 | 64 | 72 |
| x 9 | 9 | 18 | 27 | 36 | 45 | 54 | 63 | 72 | 81 |
| x 10 | 10 | 20 | 30 | 40 | 50 | 60 | 70 | 80 | 90 |

## Homework ▪ Unit 1

**1**  one thousand, two hundred and four

two thousand, one hundred and four

four thousand, two hundred and one

one thousand, four hundred and two

two thousand, four hundred and one

**2**  6765  is  6000 + 700 + 60 + 5

3921  is  3000 + 900 + 20 + 1

2743  is  2000 + 700 + 40 + 3

9364  is  9000 + 300 + 60 + 4

5430  is  5000 + 400 + 30 + 0

**3**  Any of the following:

389   398   839   893   938   983

**4**  Children's answers may vary.

800

Children's answers may vary.

200

30

## Homework ▪ Unit 2

**1**  12   3   11

**2**  No answers required.

**3**  70 + 80   = 70 + 70 + 10

120 + 130 = 120 + 120 + 10

230 + 250 = 230 + 230 + 20

440 + 410 = 410 + 410 + 30

**4**  3 + 7 + 9 + 4 = 23

6 + 4 + 5 + 9 = 24

9 + 2 + 7 + 6 = 24

3 + 6 + 8 + 9 = 26

7 + 4 + 6 + 2 = 19

9 + 5 + 8 + 7 = 29

4 + 9 + 9 + 6 = 28

3 + 4 + 8 + 6 = 21

9 + 6 + 5 + 4 = 24

**5**  Any of the following:

| | |
|---|---|
| 3 + 4 = 7 | 17 − 6 = 11 |
| 17 − 4 = 13 | 15 − 3 = 12 |
| 15 − 4 = 11 | 19 − 15 = 4 |
| 19 − 6 = 13 | |

Other totals:

| | |
|---|---|
| 3 + 6 = 9 | 4 + 6 = 10 |
| 3 + 17 = 20 | 4 + 15 = 19 |
| 3 + 15 = 18 | 4 + 17 = 21 |
| 3 + 19 = 22 | 4 + 19 = 23 |
| | |
| 6 + 15 = 21 | 15 + 17 = 32 |
| 6 + 17 = 23 | 15 + 19 = 34 |
| 6 + 19 = 25 | 17 + 19 = 36 |
| | |
| 4 − 3 = 1 | 17 − 6 = 9 |
| 6 − 3 = 3 | 19 − 3 = 16 |
| 15 − 6 = 9 | 19 − 4 = 15 |
| 17 − 3 = 14 | |

## Homework ▪ Unit 3

**1**  108  208  308  408  508  608

964  954  944  934  924  914

165  175  185  195  205  215

432  422  412  402  392  382

74  174  274  374  474  574

**2**  12 + 23 = 35      67 + 13 = 80

76 + 18 = 94      42 + 56 = 98

**3**  Children's answers may vary.

**4**  45 + 36 = 45 + 30 + 6

72 + 27 = 72 + 20 + 7

34 + 53 = 53 + 30 + 4

23 + 96 = 96 + 20 + 3

75 + 31 = 75 + 30 + 1

**5**  Any of the following:

22      26      28

72      76      78

92      96      98

## Homework ▪ Unit 4

**1**

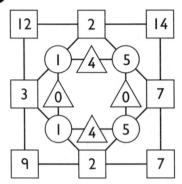

**2** mast: 35 mm     sail: 35 mm
height of boat: 8 mm
length of boat: 45 mm

**3** 48 cm     1·6 m     7·5 m

**4** Any of the following:

| | |
|---|---|
| 10 + 90 | 20 + 80 |
| 30 + 70 | 40 + 60 |
| 10 + 20 + 70 | 10 + 30 + 60 |
| 10 + 40 + 50 | 20 + 30 + 50 |
| 10 + 20 + 30 + 40 | |

## Homework ▪ Unit 5

**1** triangles     15
right-angles     38
rectangles     15

**2** No answers required.

**3**

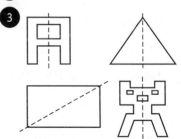

**4** 4 + 8 + 8 = 20
4 + 5 + 6 = 15
8 + 3 = 11

## Homework ▪ Unit 6

**1** 7 + 8 + 9 = 24
15 + 16 + 17 = 48
10 + 11 + 12 = 33
27 + 28 + 29 = 84
30 + 31 + 32 = 93

**2** 37 sheep

**3** 6 → 12 → 24 → 48
11 → 22 → 44 → 88
9 → 18 → 36 → 72

**4**

| | | |
|---|---|---|
| 14 + 3 | 7 + 10 | 6 + 11 |
| 9 + 8 | 16 + 1 | 5 + 12 |

**5** 1 + 4 + 8 = 13
1 + 2 + 8 + 16 = 27
1 + 4 + 16 = 21
1 + 8 + 16 = 25
1 + 2 + 4 = 7
Other totals may vary.

## Homework ▪ Unit 7

**1**

| 7 | 14 | 21 | 28 | 35 | 42 | 49 |
|---|---|---|---|---|---|---|
| 46 | 66 | 86 | 106 | 126 | 146 | 166 |
| 920 | 910 | 900 | 890 | 880 | 870 | 860 |
| -3 | -2 | -1 | 0 | 1 | 2 | 3 |
| 15 | 10 | 5 | 0 | -5 | -10 | -15 |

**2** **even:**    14 − 6    17 + 7    9 + 3
          47 − 7    42 + 24    6 + 6
**odd:**    81 − 6    231 + 530

**3** 21

**4** smallest odd   45     largest odd   63
smallest even   54     largest even   72

# Homework ▪ Unit 8

**1**    32    190    46    426

**2**

| | |
|---|---|
| **1.** $5 \times 4 = 20$ <br> **3.** $20 \div 4 = 5$ | **2.** $4 \times 5 = 20$ <br> **4.** $20 \div 5 = 4$ |
| **1.** $6 \times 4 = 24$ <br> **3.** $24 \div 4 = 6$ | **2.** $4 \times 6 = 24$ <br> **4.** $24 \div 6 = 4$ |
| **1.** $3 \times 5 = 15$ <br> **3.** $15 \div 5 = 3$ | **2.** $5 \times 3 = 15$ <br> **4.** $15 \div 3 = 5$ |
| **1.** $7 \times 8 = 56$ <br> **3.** $56 \div 8 = 7$ | **2.** $8 \times 7 = 56$ <br> **4.** $56 \div 7 = 8$ |

**3**

$12 \times 10 = 120$    $120 \div 2 = 60$    $12 \times 5 = 60$
$16 \times 10 = 160$    $160 \div 2 = 80$    $16 \times 5 = 80$
$20 \times 10 = 200$    $200 \div 2 = 100$
$200 \times 5 = 100$

**4**   No answers required.

# Homework ▪ Unit 9

**1**
$1 \times 5 = 5$      $27 \div 9 = 3$
$3 \times 5 = 15$     $36 \div 9 = 4$
$5 \times 5 = 25$     $45 \div 9 = 5$
$7 \times 5 = 35$     $54 \div 9 = 6$
$9 \times 5 = 45$     $63 \div 9 = 7$

**2**   6

**3**

| × | 10 | 6 | |
|---|----|---|---|
| 5 | 50 | 30 | → 80 |

| × | 10 | 1 | |
|---|----|---|---|
| 4 | 40 | 4 | → 44 |

| × | 10 | 1 | |
|---|----|---|---|
| 7 | 70 | 7 | → 77 |

**4**   $12 \times 3 = 36$
$9 \times 3 = 27$
$4 \times 3 = 12$
$7 \times 3 = 21$

**5**   $42 = 7 \times 6$
$48 = 8 \times 6$
$56 = 7 \times 8$
$63 = 7 \times 9$
$72 = 8 \times 9$

Any of the following:
$4 \times 7 = 28$     $11 \times 7 = 77$
$4 \times 8 = 32$     $8 \times 11 = 88$
$4 \times 9 = 36$     $9 \times 6 = 54$
$4 \times 6 = 24$     $9 \times 11 = 99$
$4 \times 11 = 44$    $6 \times 11 = 66$

# Homework ▪ Unit 10

**1**   $\frac{5}{8}$   $\frac{1}{4}$   $\frac{5}{12}$   $\frac{1}{3}$   $\frac{2}{5}$

Shaded part is pie left.

**2**

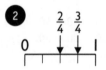

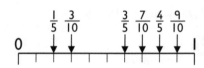

**3**   23     708     868

**4**   No answers required.

**5**   $\frac{3}{4}$ of 12 is 9      $\frac{3}{4}$ of 44 is 33

    $\frac{3}{4}$ of 60 is 45     $\frac{3}{4}$ of 200 is 150

## Homework ▪ Unit 11

1. school starts → 9:15
   lunch time → 12:30
   school ends → 3:30
   midnight → 12:00
   time to get up → 7:30.

2. 6th, 13th, 20th or 27th June

3. $5 \times 9 = 45$   $4 \times 7 = 28$
   $7 \times 8 = 56$
   Any of the following:
   $2 \times 18 = 3 \times 12 = 4 \times 9 = 6 \times 6 = 36$

4. The time will be 10:25.
   The time must be 9:55.
   So we've been driving for 45 minutes.

## Homework ▪ Unit 12

1. $6 + 5 + 6 + 9 = 26$
   $7 + 6 + 7 + 8 = 28$
   $7 + 8 + 5 + 8 = 28$
   $8 + 9 + 6 + 9 = 32$
   $9 + 8 + 5 + 8 = 30$
   $6 + 7 + 8 + 9 = 30$

2. 

| Lisa | 0 |
|------|---|
| Joe | ⵏⵏⵏ 11 |
| Raj | 111 |
| Ann | ⵏⵏⵏ 1 |

3. $-12$   $-5$   $6$   $16$   $295$   $367$

4. Children's answers may vary.

5. No answers required.

## Homework ▪ Unit 13

1. $23 \to 230$   $41 \to 410$
   $100 \to 1000$   $37 \to 370$   $64 \to 640$

2. $6 \to 60 \to 600 \to 6000 \to 60\,000$

3. No answers required.

4. 60   260   20   880

5. $(3 + 5) \times 10 = 80$
   $(5 + 6) \times 10 = 110$
   $(4 + 5 + 6) \times 10 = 150$
   **or**
   $(1 + 3 + 4) \times 10 = 80$
   $(1 + 4 + 6) \times 10 = 110$
   $(1 + 3 + 5 + 6) \times 10 = 150$

## Homework ▪ Unit 14

1. $25 + 17 = 42$
   $325 - 234 = 91$
   $231 - 41 = 190$
   $577 + 33 = 610$

2. No answers required.

3. $25 \to 75$
   $33 \to 67$
   $27 \to 73$
   $90 \to 10$
   $14 \to 86$

4. $39 + 17 = 56$
   $31 + 39 = 70$
   $16 + 31 + 26 = 73$
   $41 + 39 + 61 = 141$

5. £3.60

## Homework ▪ Unit 15

**1** $321 + 20 = 341$  $245 - 12 = 233$
$300 + 20 = 320$

**2** $(3 \times 4) + (10 \times 2) + (7 \times 1)$
$= 39$ goals

**3** $£2.40 + £1.95 = £4.35$  $£2.95$ left
$£2.40 + £1.80 = £4.20$  $£3.10$ left
$£3.50 + £1.80 = £5.30$  $£2.00$ left
$£1.95 + £1.80 = £3.75$  $£3.55$ left

**4**

| 47 | 35 | 61 | → 143 |
|-----|-----|-----|-----|
| 99 | 7 | 134 | → 240 |
| 420 | 116 | 70 | → 606 |

↓ ↓ ↓ ↓        ↘
488 566 158 265    124

**5** Any of the following:

$301 - 21 = 280$
$301 - 43 = 258$
$301 - 70 = 231$
$187 - 21 = 166$
$187 - 43 = 144$
$187 - 70 = 117$
$460 - 21 = 439$
$460 - 43 = 417$
$460 - 70 = 390$

## Homework ▪ Unit 16

**1** pencil → 10 g
apple → 120 g
tin of beans → 480 g
elephant → 4000 kg
footballer → 85 kg

**2** 70 g → 30 g, 20 g, 20 g
50 g → 30 g, 20 g

120 g → 30 g, 30 g, 20 g, 20 g, 20 g
100 g → 30 g, 30 g, 20 g, 20 g

**3** $\frac{1}{2}$ litre → 2 cups

250 ml → 4 cups
25 ml → 40 cups
50 ml → 20 cups
100 ml → 10 cups

**4** 1 kg → 2 boxes of 500 g
240 g → 2 boxes of 120 g
18 g → 2 boxes of 9 g
310 g → 2 boxes of 155 g

**5** Children's answers may vary.

## Homework ▪ Unit 17

**1** triangle = 7
pentagon = 69
square = 12
circle = 11

**2** cube → square
cuboid → rectangle, square
cylinder → circle
square-based pyramid → triangle, square
triangular prism → rectangle, triangle
hemisphere → circle

**3** No answers required.

**4** Children's answers may vary.

**5** odd box  173  771  2301
even box  894  4700  2318  3572

## Homework ▪ Unit 18

**1** 16 km

**2** 21 stamps, 4p change

**3**　16 → 47　86 → 55
　29 → 60　105 → 74

**4**
　　　32
　　　28
　　　39

42　32　25

lion → 14
ladybird → 7
lizard → 11

## Homework ▪ Unit 19

**1**　89 → 11
　66 → 34
　51 → 49
　17 → 83
　45 → 55

**2**　140 + 100 = 240
　150 + 120 = 270 **or** 160 + 110 = 270
　160 + 150 = 310

Any of the following:
160 + 140 = 300　160 + 100 = 260
150 + 140 = 290　150 + 110 = 260
150 + 100 = 250
140 + 120 = 260　140 + 110 = 250
120 + 110 = 230　120 + 100 = 220
110 + 100 = 210

**3**　−15°C　−4°C　−2°C　0°C　6°C

**4**　17 → 34 → 16 → 260
　189 → 378 → 360 → 604
　381 → 762 → 744 → 988

**5**　160 ÷ 4 = 40
　This number is an integer.
　173 ÷ 5 = 34·6
　This number is not an integer.

970 ÷ 2 = 485
This number is an integer.
4·5 + 4·5 + 2·5 = 11·5
This number is not an integer.

## Homework ▪ Unit 20

**1**
$7 \times 12 = (7 \times 10 = 70) + (7 \times 2 = 14)$
$70 + 14 = 84$

$7 \times 13 = (7 \times 10 = 70) + (7 \times 3 = 21)$
$70 + 21 = 91$

$7 \times 24 = (7 \times 20 = 140) + (7 \times 4 = 28)$
$140 + 28 = 168$

$7 \times 32 = (7 \times 30 = 210) + (7 \times 2 = 14)$
$210 + 14 = 224$

**2**　No answers required.

**3**　72 ÷ 12 = 6
　112 ÷ 7 = 16
　568 ÷ 8 = 71
　171 ÷ 9 = 19
　Children's answers may vary.

**4**　32p

## Homework ▪ Unit 21

**1**　Children's answers may vary.

**2**　13 friends

**3**　123 → 120　　84 → 80
　119 → 120　　71 → 70
　77 → 80　　　117 → 120

**4**　6 bags

**5**　192 slices　108 slices　68 slices

## Homework ▪ Unit 22

**1** 0  1·3  2·5  3·1  5·2  54  54·1

**2** £15.24

**3** Any of the following:

| 9 | 9 | 9 | 8 | 8 | 8 |
|---|---|---|---|---|---|
| 9 | 9 | 9 | 8 | 8 | 7 |
| 9 | 9 | 9 | 8 | 7 | 7 |
| 9 | 9 | 9 | 7 | 7 | 7 |
| 9 | 9 | 8 | 8 | 8 | 7 |
| 9 | 9 | 8 | 8 | 7 | 7 |
| 9 | 9 | 8 | 7 | 7 | 7 |
| 9 | 8 | 8 | 8 | 7 | 7 |
| 9 | 8 | 8 | 7 | 7 | 7 |
| 8 | 8 | 8 | 7 | 7 | 7 |

**4**
$49 + 49 + 49 = 147$
$49 + 49 + 27 = 125$
$49 + 49 + 12 = 110$
$49 + 27 + 27 = 103$

**5**
$\frac{3}{4} \rightarrow 0·75$

$\frac{1}{5} \rightarrow 0·2$

$9\frac{4}{10} \rightarrow 9·4$

## Homework ▪ Unit 23

**1** Children's answers may vary.

**2** No answers required.

**3** 57p

**4**

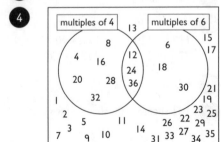

**5**

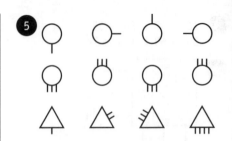

This pattern can also logically revert to its first phase.

## Homework ▪ Unit 24

**1**
$377 + 437 = 814$
$631 - 154 = 477$
$504 \div 9 = 56$
$67 \times 5 = 335$

**2** £7.42

**3** 6

**4** In the pattern I can count 11 horizontal lines, 15 vertical lines, 2 diagonal lines.

**5** No answers required.

## Homework ▪ Unit 25

**1**

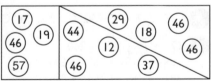

**2** 798  809  880  899  908  970  978  989

**3** No answers required.

**4** 547    606
     597    601

## Homework ▪ Unit 26

**1** 66 − 19 = 47
403 − 342 = 61
433 − 197 = 236
681 − 328 = 353

**2**

even number + even number = even number
odd number + odd number = even number
even number − even number = even number
odd number − odd number = even number

**3**

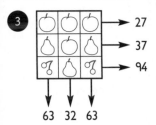

     → 27
     → 37
     → 94

63   32   63

apple → 9
pear → 14
cherries → 40

**4** 79 + 231 + 94 = 230 + 90 + 70 +
9 + 5
69 + 99 + 49 = 100 + 70 + 50 − 3
14 + 672 + 210 = 672 + 200 + 20 + 4
78 + 105 + 99 = 199 + 5 + 70 + 8

**5** Any of the following:
£3.50, £2.50, £1.60, £1.55, £1.52, £1.51
£3.20, £2.20, £1.30, £1.25, £1.22, £1.21
£2.90, £1.90, £1, 95p, 92p, 91p
£2.60, £1.60, 70p, 65p, 62p, 61p

## Homework ▪ Unit 27

**1** 672 − 89 = 865 − 282
393 − 326 = 353 − 286
532 − 278 = 731 − 477

**2** had £5;      got £3.22 change
had £7.15;    got £5.37 change
had £10.00;   got £8.22 change
had £9.99;    got £8.21 change

**3** 115 pens

**4** ten      kite      kitten      net
Other words may vary.

**5** 180 runs

## Homework ▪ Unit 28

**1** The area of a cornflake is about 1 cm$^2$.
The area of a piece of toast is about
144 cm$^2$ (or 100 cm$^2$).
The area of a homework sheet is
about 600 cm$^2$.
The area of a squashed grape is about
9 cm$^2$.

**2** 280 min = 4 hr 40 min

**3** 224 pages

**4** square 80 mm, triangle 72 mm,
pentagon 70 mm, hexagon 72 mm

**5** 17 → × 3 → 51 → + 6 → 57
17 → × 7 → 119 → + 77 → 196

## Homework ▪ Unit 29

**1** hour hand at 12, minute hand at 9

**2** line dividing face into two sets
(10, 11, 12, 1, 2, 3) and
(4, 5, 6, 7, 8, 9)

**3**  $6 \times 48p = 288p$
$48 \times 6p = 288p$
$9p \times 17 = 153p$
$17p \times 9 = 153p$
$19p \times 7 = 133p$
$7 \times 19p = 133p$

**4**  Jill

**5**  shape 4: 16      shape 5: 25
shape 6: 36      shape 7: 49

## Homework ▪ Unit 30

**1**  5 of each coin

**2**  $17 \times 9 = 153$      $13 \times 9 = 117$
$15 - 13 = 2$      $15 \times 7 = 105$
$6 \times 7 = 42$      $6 + 17 = 23$

**3**  14 boxes

**4**  70p

**5**  $7 \rightarrow 35 \rightarrow 28 \rightarrow 56 \rightarrow 97 \rightarrow 96$

## Homework ▪ Unit 31

**1**  44 spiders      352 legs
36 dogs      144 legs
29 starfish      145 legs
197 chickens      394 legs

**2**  2560 min = 42 hr 40 min  impossible

**3**  watch → £4.86
juice carton → 49p
juice bottle → 59p
book → £1.53
bear → £5.73
racquet → £10.80

**4**  $1 + 2 + 3 + 4 = 10$
$3 + 4 + 10 + 30$ **or**
$40 + 4 + 2 + 1 = 47$

$1 + 3 + 30 + 40$ **or**
$40 + 20 + 10 + 4 = 74$

$4 + 20 + 30 + 40 = 94$

$2 + 3 + 4 + 40 = 49$

**5**  Children's answers may vary.

## Homework ▪ Unit 32

**1**  $333 \div 9 = 37$
$648 \div 12 = 54$
$5040 \div 120 = 42$

**2**  Buy boxes          apples
Buy individually    lemons, mangoes,
pears

**3**  $6 \times 9 = 2 \times 3 \times 9$
$7 \times 3 \times 2 = 6 \times 7$
$5 \times 2 \times 5 = 10 \times 5$
$8 \times 7 = 2 \times 4 \times 7$
$3 \times 3 \times 3 \times 3 = 9 \times 9$

**4**

| half of the number | number | double the number |
|---|---|---|
| 151 | 302 | 604 |
| 198 | 396 | 792 |
| 525 | 1050 | 2100 |
| 351 | 702 | 1404 |
| 333 | 666 | 1332 |

**5**  1020 sneezes

# Homework ▪ Unit 33

**1**  18 km

**2**  $63 \times 7 = 441$    $31 \times 9 = 279$
$122 \times 8 = 976$    $726 \div 6 = 121$
$921 \div 3 = 307$

**3**  216 matchsticks

**4**  $300 \rightarrow 3000$
$78 \cdot 1 \rightarrow 781$
$21 \rightarrow 210$
$401 \rightarrow 4010$
$27 \cdot 5 \rightarrow 275$

multiply by 10

**5**  poisonous pie: 139

# Homework ▪ Unit 34

**1**  Flap: 30 worms    Flop: 50 worms

**2**  15  46  132  97  243

**3**  64

**4**  29 children

**5**  The 8 ball went through the × 8 gate
$8 \times 8 = 64$
The 9 ball went through the × 8 gate
$9 \times 8 = 72$
The 10 ball went through the + 8
gate $10 + 8 = 18$
$14 + 64 + 72 + 18 = 168$
Higher score: Children's answers
may vary.

# Homework ▪ Unit 35

**1**  122 people with 20p left over

**2**  $A = 7$      $B = 5$      $C = 12$
$B + B = 10$  $C - B = 7$ (or A)

**3**  24          64          760

**4**  55 matches

$(10 + 9 + 8 + 7 + 6 + 5 + 4 + 3 + 2 + 1)$

**5**  Hot dog stall took £54.00
'Soak the teacher' took £49.50
Face painting took £18.70
Total £122.20

# Homework ▪ Unit 36

**1**
| | | |
|---|---|---|
| red | blue | white |
| red | white | blue |
| blue | red | white |
| blue | white | red |
| white | red | blue |
| white | blue | red |

**2**  £2.22  £8.16  £88.50  £210.05

**3**  36 bricks

**4**
| | |
|---|---|
| South Africa v Pakistan | 7th July |
| Pakistan v Kenya | 10th July |
| Kenya v India | 7th July |
| Kenya v South Africa | 3rd July |

**5**  66

## My Maths Diary ▪ Unit 1

**1** 995 → 996

four thousand and three → 4004
thousand and four

six thousand, two hundred and
nineteen → 6220

3199 → 3200

**2** 1490 ← 1500
2599 ← 2609
3990 ← 4000

two thousand, nine hundred and
ninety-eight ← 3008

nine thousand and two ← 9012

**3** People on a full double-decker   100
Slices in a loaf of bread               20
Words on page 1 of this book   200

## My Maths Diary ▪ Unit 2

**1** 70 + 80 = 150   80 + 70 = 150
150 − 70 = 80   150 − 80 = 70

**2** The quicker calculations should be:
779 + 1            86 + 23
3 + 7 + 15      6 + 4 + 8 + 2

**3** 25 → 50     24 → 48
27 → 54     36 → 72

## My Maths Diary ▪ Unit 3

**1** 61 → 68     6001 → 6008
98 → 105    593 → 600   8372 → 8379

**2** 502, 499 → 3
52, 49 → 3
5002, 4999 → 3

3786, 3789 → 3
169, 174 → 5
7003,  6998 → 5

**3** 704 − 8 = 694        incorrect
should be 696

6998 + 7 = 700 015  incorrect
should be 7005

803 − 796 = 193      incorrect
should be 7

5000 − 7 = 4 000 993 incorrect
should be 4993

567 − 9 = 558          correct

7005 − 6996 = 11     incorrect
should be 9

## My Maths Diary ▪ Unit 4

**1** Children's answers may vary.

**2** My friend's height                1·5 m

The width of my thumb        10 mm

The distance from London
to Manchester                     250 km

**3** 250 cm → 2·50 m
125 cm → 1·25 m
3250 cm → 32·50 m

## My Maths Diary ▪ Unit 5

**1** Children should tick the following:
triangle; parallelogram; trapezium;
octagon.

**2** Children's answers may vary.
Check that the shapes they draw meet the requirements given.

An equilateral triangle should have all sides equal.

An isosceles triangle should have two sides equal.

**3**

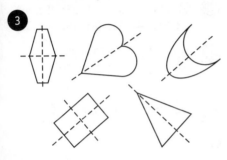

## My Maths Diary ▪ Unit 6

**1** $28 + 67 = 95$

**2** $82 - 39 = 43$

**3** Children's answers may vary.

## My Maths Diary ▪ Unit 7

**1** 47, 50, 53, 56, 59, 62, 65
159, 161, 163, 165, 167, 169, 171
974, 980, 986, 992, 998, 1004, 1010

**2**

**3** Odd numbers: 899 643 861 265

## My Maths Diary ▪ Unit 8

**1**
| | |
|---|---|
| $4 \times 5 = 20$ | $10 \times 6 = 60$ |
| $3 \times 5 = 15$ | $8 \times 10 = 80$ |
| $5 \times 5 = 25$ | $9 \times 2 = 18$ |
| $10 \times 10 = 100$ | $6 \times 5 = 30$ |

**2** $31 \rightarrow 62 \quad 25 \rightarrow 50 \quad 310 \rightarrow 620$
$3100 \rightarrow 6200 \quad 450 \rightarrow 900 \quad 4800 \rightarrow 9600$

**3** $8 \rightarrow 32 \quad 9 \rightarrow 36 \quad 7 \rightarrow 28$
$25 \rightarrow 100 \quad 14 \rightarrow 56 \quad 60 \rightarrow 240$

## My Maths Diary ▪ Unit 9

**1** Children's answers may vary.

**2** Children's answers may vary.

**3**
| | |
|---|---|
| $7 \times 3 = 21$ | $3 \times 6 = 18$ |
| $3 \times 10 = 30$ | $5 \times 8 = 40$ |
| $5 \times 25 = 125$ | $4 \times 20 = 80$ |
| $5 \times 20 = 100$ | $8 \times 3 = 24$ |

## My Maths Diary ▪ Unit 10

**1** $\frac{1}{2}$ of 24 is 12 $\qquad \frac{1}{3}$ of 24 is 8

$\frac{1}{6}$ of 24 is 4 $\qquad \frac{1}{4}$ of 24 is 6

**2** Larger fractions to be ringed are:

$\frac{3}{4} \quad \frac{1}{3} \quad \frac{1}{2} \quad \frac{5}{6} \quad \frac{1}{4} \quad \frac{1}{3}$

**3** $\frac{1}{2} + \frac{1}{2} = 1 \qquad \frac{2}{6} + \frac{2}{3} = 1$

$\frac{1}{3} + \frac{2}{3} = 1 \qquad \frac{2}{4} + \frac{1}{2} = 1$

## My Maths Diary ▪ Unit 11

**1** The clock should be joined to the watch showing 5:15.

**2** Children's answers may vary.

**3** 45 minutes, with any luck.

## My Maths Diary ▪ Unit 12

**1**

| Ways of getting to school | Tally | Total |
|---|---|---|
| Walking | ////  ////  /// | 13 |
| Bus | /// | 3 |
| Car | ////  ////  / | 11 |

**2**

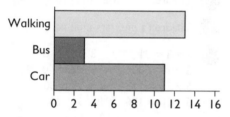

Walking
Bus
Car

0  2  4  6  8  10  12  14  16

**3** 1. 20   2. 15

## My Maths Diary ▪ Unit 13

**1**
62 → 620      34 → 340
78 → 780      894 → 8940
9 → 90        11 → 110
101 → 1010    60 → 600
81 → 810

**2**

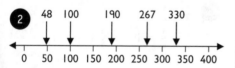

48  100    190  267  330

0  50  100  150  200  250  300  350  400

**3** 548 → 550  671 → 670  37 → 40
11 → 10    765 → 770

## My Maths Diary ▪ Unit 14

**1** 30 + 60 = 90   500 + 700 = 1200
40 + 70 + 60 = 170
6000 + 3000 = 9000
4000 + 8000 = 12 000
300 + 800 + 700 = 1800
2000 + 3000 + 8000 = 13 000

**2** (62, 38) (70, 30) (75, 25) (52, 48)
(19, 81) (44, 56) (81, 19) (63, 37)

**3** 350 + 650      150 + 850
750 + 250      450 + 550

## My Maths Diary ▪ Unit 15

**1**

| 3 | 5 | 7 | 5 | = 20 |
|---|---|---|---|---|
| 6 | 12 | 8 | 4 | = 30 |
| 4 | 3 | 2 | 16 | = 25 |
| 7 | 2 | 3 | 15 | = 27 |
| = 20 | = 22 | = 20 | = 40 | |

**2** Children's answers may vary.

**3** 12 + 21 = 33      39 + 22 = 61
34 + 51 = 85      49 + 18 = 67
61 + 36 = 97      33 + 59 = 92
25 + 61 = 86      41 + 59 = 100

## My Maths Diary ▪ Unit 16

**1** Children's answers may vary.

**2** The mass of a small bar of chocolate: 100 g

The mass of a heavy suitcase: 20 kg

The amount of medicine in a spoon: 5 ml

## My Maths Diary ▪ Unit 17

**1** Children should tick these shapes:
cube; cuboid; triangular prism;
hexagonal prism

**2** 6 cubes    8 cubes    8 cubes

**3**

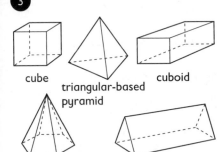

cube

triangular-based
pyramid

cuboid

hexagonal-based
pyramid

triangular prism

## My Maths Diary ▪ Unit 18

**1** Children's answers may vary.

**2** Answers from:
4 × 6 = 24     6 × 4 = 24
24 ÷ 6 = 4     24 ÷ 4 = 6

**3** 27 × 2 = 54

## My Maths Diary ▪ Unit 19

**1** Positive integers: 10, 11, 12, 13, 14,
15, 16, 17, 18, 19, 20

Negative integers: −10, −11, −12, −13,
−14, −15, −16, −17, −18, −19, −20

## My Maths Diary ▪ Unit 20

**1** & **2**

The calculations that children can do
quickly will vary. The answers to all the
calculations are given below.

| | | |
|---|---|---|
| 6 × 10 = 60 | 5 × 9 = 45 | 10 × 8 = 80 |
| 9 × 7 = 63 | 9 × 2 = 18 | 8 × 9 = 72 |
| 7 × 10 = 70 | 6 × 5 = 30 | 4 × 7 = 28 |
| 10 × 9 = 90 | 9 × 9 = 81 | 6 × 9 = 54 |

**3** 8 × 9 = 72        8 × 12 = 96
8 × 13 = 104      8 × 15 = 120

## My Maths Diary ▪ Unit 21

**1** 6 → 120  5 → 100  8 → 160  10 → 200
3 → 60  9 → 180  4 → 80  12 → 240

**2** 23 × 8 ≈ 160
25 × 6 ≈ 180
19 × 9 ≈ 180
22 × 7 ≈ 140

**3** 26 × 4 = 104

## My Maths Diary ▪ Unit 22

**1**

0  0·1  0·2  0·3  0·4  0·5  0·6  0·7  0·8  0·9  1·0

**2** Fractions circled: $\frac{1}{6}$ $\frac{1}{3}$ $\frac{1}{4}$ $\frac{1}{8}$ $\frac{3}{8}$

**3** Larger number of pair:
0·6   5·3   2·1   6·0   25·7

My Maths Diary

## My Maths Diary ▪ Unit 23

**1**

| Shapes | Tally |
|--------|-------|
| pentagon | 5 |
| triangle | 9 |
| circle | 6 |

**2** Children's answers will vary.

**3** 21: in intersection of circles and top right-hand box
18: in left-hand circle only and top right-hand box

## My Maths Diary ▪ Unit 24

**1** Children's answers may vary.

**2**

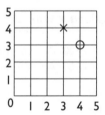

**3** east → south-east → south-west → east → north

## My Maths Diary ▪ Unit 25

**1** 4568 < 4586
1995 > 1985
6392 < 6923

**2**

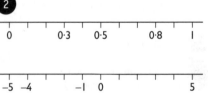

**3** 603 → 600   750 → 800   149 → 100
377 → 400   209 → 200

## My Maths Diary ▪ Unit 26

**1** 207 + 3 + 104 + 63 + 8 = 385

**2** Check the children's working.

**3** Answers from:
£4.29 + £2.99 = £7.28
£4.29 + £1.52 = £5.81
£4.29 + 74p = £5.03
£2.99 + £1.52 = £4.51
£2.99 + 74p = £3.73
£1.52 + 74p = £2.26

## My Maths Diary ▪ Unit 27

**1** Any of the following:

| | |
|---|---|
| 399 − 49 = 350 | 399 − 60 = 339 |
| 399 − 38 = 361 | 399 − 51 = 348 |
| 583 − 49 = 534 | 583 − 60 = 523 |
| 583 − 38 = 545 | 583 − 51 = 532 |
| 750 − 49 = 701 | 750 − 60 = 690 |
| 750 − 38 = 712 | 750 − 51 = 699 |
| 804 − 49 = 755 | 804 − 60 = 744 |
| 804 − 38 = 766 | 804 − 51 = 753 |

**2** Children's answers may vary.

**3** Children's answers may vary.

## My Maths Diary ▪ Unit 28

**1** square: 120 mm
hexagon: 120 mm
triangle: 90 mm

**2** 8 square centimetres

**3** Children's answers may vary.

## My Maths Diary ▪ Unit 29

**1** NE → SW: two right angles

4 o'clock → 7 o'clock: one right angle

WASH → OFF: three right angles

**2**

45 degrees

90 degrees

30 degrees

60 degrees

**3** Check the angle is 45°.

## My Maths Diary ▪ Unit 30

**1** Children's answers will vary.

**2** Children's answers will vary.

**3** $398 + 59 = 457$    $467 + 85 = 552$

## My Maths Diary ▪ Unit 31

**1** $11 + 12 = 23$

**2** Children's answers may vary.

Sequence increases by two each time or sequence is the odd numbers. $2n - 1$.

The 10th shape has 19 circles and the 20th shape has 39 circles.

## My Maths Diary ▪ Unit 32

**1** $36 \div 3 = 12$      $24 \div 4 = 6$
$90 \div 10 = 9$      $45 \div 5 = 9$
$280 \div 2 = 140$

**2** $23 \times 8 = 184$

| × | 20 | 3 | |
|---|-----|-----|-----|
| 8 | 160 | 24 | = 184 |

**3** $25 \times 5 = 125$      $41 \times 3 = 123$
$28 \times 6 = 168$      $49 \times 5 = 245$

## My Maths Diary ▪ Unit 33

**1** $4 \times 24 = 96$ – Yes

**2** $96 \div 6 = 16$

**3** $39 \div 6 = 6$ remainder 3
Mr Brown needs 7 boxes.

$50 \div 8 = 6$ remainder 2
Mrs Green fills 6 bags.

## My Maths Diary ▪ Unit 34

**1** 12 squares shaded

**2** 5 squares shaded

**3** $\frac{1}{2}$ bottle    $\frac{3}{4}$ cake

## My Maths Diary ▪ Unit 35

**1** 4 and 5

**2** 23 stickers and 17p change

**3** 15 people stood
$25 \times 8 = 200$ and $215 - 200 = 15$

## My Maths Diary ▪ Unit 36

**1** 1 hr 30 mins

**2**

| Train timetable | | |
|---|---|---|
| **Station** | **a.m.** | **p.m.** |
| Bentley | 9:10 | 2:40 |
| Orton | 9:30 | 3:00 |
| Amble | 9:50 | 3:20 |

**3** Any of the following:

| | |
|---|---|
| Sunfun, Dairy Delight and Frosted Frizzle | £1.95 |
| Sunfun, Dairy Delight and Magnice | £2.30 |
| Sunfun, Frosted Frizzle and Magnice | £2.50 |
| Dairy Delight, Frosted Frizzle and Magnice | £2.70 |